CIRIA C692

Environmental good practice on site (third edition)

Edited by

Iain Audus

Philip Charles

Simon Evans

Environmental good practice on site (third edition)

Audus, I, Charles, P, Evans, S (editors)

CIRIA C692   © CIRIA 2010   ISBN 978-0-86017-692-6

First printed as C502, 1999   Reprinted 2000, 2001, 2002

Revised as C650, 2005

British Library Cataloguing in Publication Data

A catalogue record is available for this book from the British Library.

Keywords
Environmental good practice, pollution prevention, recycling and reclaimed materials, regulation, risk and value management, site management, supply chain management, sustainable construction, sustainable resource use, waste minimisation, water quality, water resources

Reader interest	Classification	
Planning, design and management of construction site works	Availability	Unrestricted
	Content	Advice/guidance
	Status	Committee-guided
	Users	Construction professionals and managers

Published by CIRIA, Classic House, 174–180 Old Street, London EC1V 9BP, UK

This third edition updates the second edition (CIRIA C650, 2005), and has been undertaken in collaboration with a project steering group of industry practitioners.

Funders

This update was funded by BAM Nuttall, Bovis Lend Lease, WRAP, and the CIRIA Core members programme.

Project steering group

CIRIA wishes to express its thanks to the members of the group for their contributions to the guide:

Full members

Beverley Lister	Beverley Lister Associates Ltd*
Ross Fairley	Burges Salmon
Simon Tilling	Burges Salmon
John Hutton	BAM Nuttall
John Davies	Davis Langdon LLP*
Bridget Plowright	ConstructionSkills
Gareth Brown	Bovis Lend Lease (chair)
Adam Spencer	Defence Estates*
Andrew Powell	Environment Agency
Stewart Smith	Galliford Try (formerly)*
Paul Thomas	Galliford Try
Steve Livingstone	Jackson Civil Engineering*
John O'Reilly	Kier*
Judith Johnston	Northern Ireland Environment Agency
Nicola Ashworth	Parsons Brinckerhoff
Alastair McNeill	Scottish Environment Protection Agency (formerly)*
Vicki Walsh	Sir Robert McAlpine
Jim Wiltshire	WRAP

Reviewers

Richard Gotheridge	Balfour Beatty Major Civil Engineering*
Howard Price	Chartered Institute of Environmental Health*
Peter Hinton	Institute of Field Archaeologists*

*denotes reviewer of environmental issue topic(s)

CIRIA's project manager for this update was Philip Charles.

CIRIA would like to acknowledge those involved in the development of the first edition in 1999 (C502) and the second edition in 2005 (C650).

Source materials

CIRIA is grateful to the following organisations for providing information:

Balfour Beatty	Galliford Try
Bureau Veritas	Kier
Burges Salmon	Morrison Construction
Environment Agency	Parsons Brinckerhoff.

CIRIA would like to thank the following organisations for providing photographs:

ARUP	Kier
Balfour Beatty	Morrison Construction
Bouygues Travaux Publics	MoLAS
Bovis Lend Lease	Parsons Brinckerhoff
Galliford Try	TT2 Ltd

Construction activities have the potential to impact their surroundings, including neighbours as well as the natural and built environment. Good environmental practice enables these impacts to be managed positively. Impacts can take many forms, for example effects on surrounding flora and fauna, watercourses, noise or pollution. Clients, their professional advisers, contractors and the whole construction supply chain have responsibilities for appropriate environmental management ensuring compliance with legal and other requirements.

This guide is intended to be a user-friendly reference and training aid, and provides practical advice about managing construction on site to minimise environmental impacts. It is relevant to all concerned within the construction process.

The guide is divided into four sections:

1 **Benefits and obligations**

   Outlines the benefits of good practice and the environmental obligations that a site operates under in terms of both the legislation and the contract conditions.

2 **General site management issues**

   Provides general advice on good practice, to allow a framework for managing environmental impacts on site to be established.

3 **Construction activities**

   Identifies the environmental issues that need to be considered when carrying out a particular construction activity.

4 **Environmental issues**

   Provides advice on how to manage impacts for each environmental issue and how to recognise and deal with any problems that may arise.

Further guidance documents as highlighted throughout the guide are included on the accompanying CD-Rom.

Contents

Contents

Contents

Tables

Target audience

This guide provides advice on environmental good practice for each construction stage and is aimed primarily at site personnel including subcontractors. People involved in the early stages of a project's development, including designers and planners, can influence the ability of site personnel to meet their obligations by adopting the good practice contained within this guide.

Primary audience	Secondary audience
Site managers	Client organisations
Site engineers	Estimators
Site foremen and site supervisors	Quantity surveyors
Project managers	Company directors
Contract supervisors/resident engineers	Designers
Site environmental co-ordinator	Construction planners
	All other site staff

This guide addresses issues from the point after completion of site investigation. This may have involved environmental impact assessment (EIA) and/or a strategic environmental assessment (SEA). The findings from these assessments or any other project related reports should be referred to, as the issues they highlight could affect the progress of a project.

This guide is written for a wide range of construction workers.

Section 1 Benefits and obligations

Presents the benefits of reading this guide and the reasons for adopting good environmental practice on site. Good environmental practice starts with planning for good site management.

Section 2 General site management issues

Explains how the overall establishment and management of the site can form the basis of environmental good practice. Those with management responsibility, from the initial set up of the site through to project completion and demobilisation, should read this section.

Section 3 Construction activities

Summarises the various pre-construction, construction, post-construction activities and other important issues that should be considered.

Section 4 Environmental issues

Provides more detailed advice about the particular environmental issues identified as being relevant to a particular site, such as archaeology or noise.

Use this guide with the toolbox talks (available from CECA <**www.ceca.co.uk**> and the UKCG <**www.ukcg.org.uk**>) by concentrating on the issue or construction activity most relevant to the work taking place at any given time.

How to use this guide

Throughout the guide symbols alongside the text help identify the type of information presented. These symbols and their explanations are shown in the following table:

	Case study		Legal
	Checklist		Plan ahead
	Key guidance		Reference

This guide addresses environmental issues once a project has reached the construction stage. For each of the main topics it describes the most commonly experienced issues and offers advice on how to avoid or overcome them. To assist good environmental practice on site, this guide explains how to establish a suitable management framework for the site, and how to set up central site facilities such as vehicle refuelling stations and materials storage locations.

The reader should be clear about the scope of the guide. In particular:

- □ it is not a health and safety manual
- □ it should not replace contact with regulators
- □ although it gives an overview of legislation, detailed guidance should be sought from the company's environmental representative (or external specialists) if it is required
- □ it does not deal with environmental issues that should have been covered during the planning and design of the project.

 In all instances, when dealing with the issues covered, do not take action that is beyond available expertise. If in doubt, seek specialist advice.

Generally, the advice given in the guide is relevant for all types of contract conditions, eg traditional, design and build (D&B), design-build-finance-operate (DBFO), build-operate-transfer (BOT) and Private Finance Initiatives (PFI).

Finally, the guide does not cover issues relating to the coastal and marine environment. A separate CIRIA publication covers such issues (Budd *et al*, 2003).

Relationship to other CIRIA guidance

CIRIA has produced several publications that supplement the good practice advice provided by this guide:

☐ *Archaeology and development – a good practice guide to managing risk and maximising benefit* (C672, 2008)

☐ *Assessing risks posed by hazardous ground gases to buildings* (C665, 2007)

☐ *Coastal and marine environmental site guide* (C584, 2003)

☐ *Control of water pollution from construction sites. Guidance for consultants and contractors* (C532, 2001)

☐ *Control of water pollution from linear construction projects. Technical guidance* (C648, 2006)

☐ *Environmental good practice – training resource* (C678TP, 2008)

☐ *Invasive species management for infrastructure managers and the construction industry* (C679, 2008)

☐ *Unexploded ordnance (UXO) A guide for the construction industry* (C681, 2009)

☐ *Working with wildlife: guidance for the construction industry* (C691, 2011)

Details of these publications can be found at <**www.ciria.org**>.

Abatement notices   A local authority has a duty under the Environmental Protection Act 1990 to serve an abatement notice where it is satisfied that a statutory nuisance exists.

Abstraction   The removal of water from groundwaters or surface waters, either temporarily or permanently. Permits are required from the Environment Agency in England and Wales. In Scotland the requirements of the Water Environment (Controlled Activities) (Scotland) Regulations 2005 (CAR) must be met, and may require the acquisition of a licence from the Scottish Environment Protection Agency (SEPA).

Asbestos   Banned material due to severe health implications associated with exposure. Found in many buildings as insulation material, fire retardant, used in floor and ceiling tiles, gaskets etc. Requires specialist removal and disposal. Asbestos survey required when presence is suspected before demolition.

Biodiversity   A term used to describe the variety of living things on earth. Maintaining or increasing biodiversity is a positive outcome.

Brownfield site   As opposed to a "greenfield" site, a brownfield site is a generic term for land used previously for an industrial or commercial purpose, being available for redevelopment towards new industrial, commercial or residential use. The level of remediation or clean-up necessary may vary significantly.

Climate change   The consequences upon the naturally occurring greenhouse effect arising out of man's industrial and domestic practices. There is accepted evidence that man's influence upon climate change is a reality.

Consent/licence/ permit (discharge to water)   In England and Wales any intended discharge to "controlled waters" will require permission from the environmental regulator over granting of a environmental permit. Any intended discharge to the water environment in Scotland will require permission from the SEPA over granting of controlled activity regulation (CAR) point discharge license. See *Trade effluent consent for discharge to sewers.*

Controlled waters/ water environment (Scotland)

Almost all natural waters in the UK. This includes surface water (rivers, streams, lakes, reservoirs, ditches, ponds), including those temporarily dry, and groundwater (aquifers), as well as coastal waters up to three miles out. It is an offence to pollute such waters. Responsibility for policing controlled waters is placed with the regulators. In Scotland refer to The Water Environment (Controlled Activities) (Scotland) Regulations 2005.

Contaminated land

Land that contains substances in on or under land likely to represent a hazard to humans, animals or the environment.

Dust

Airborne solid matter up to about 2 mm in size. Along with noise and odour, dust is probably the most commonly complained about issue or "statutory nuisance".

Duty of care for waste

A legal responsibility to ensure that production, storage, transporting and disposal of business waste is carried out without harming the environment.

Ecology

All living things, such as trees, flowering plants, insects, birds and mammals, and their habitats.

Enforcement notices

In England, Wales and Scotland, the environmental regulator has the power to serve a works notice on a site to prevent or remedy water pollution. Such notices can be served before pollution has occurred if, in the opinion of the environmental regulator, a polluting substance is likely to enter surface waters or groundwater. The environmental regulator may serve a works notice to ensure that waters are cleaned up after pollution has occurred. Similar consents exist in Northern Ireland and are regulated by the Northern Ireland Environment Agency (NIEA).

Environmental permit (water)	Any intended discharge to "controlled waters" in England and Wales will require permission from the Environment Agency over granting of an environmental permit. See *Trade effluent consent for discharge to sewers.*
Environmental aspect	Element of an organisations activities or products or service that can interact with the environment.
Environmental impact	Any change to the environment, whether adverse or beneficial, wholly or partially resulting from an organisation's activities
Environmental indicator	A measure of an environmental parameter, which can be used to assess the present state of the environment by looking at trends over time.
Environmental receptor	Any feature, habitat, area or living organism that potentially can be negatively affected by site activities.
European Waste Catalogue (EWC) Codes	Codes to identify various types of waste, eg Cat. 17 09 04 *Mixed construction and demolition wastes.*
Forest Stewardship Council (FSC)	An organisation that sets out international standards for the responsible management of forests in accordance with ecological, social and economic criteria.
Greenhouse gases	Naturally present and man-made gases, which contribute to the greenhouse effect. These gases include carbon dioxide, methane, and chlorofluorocarbons (CFC's).
Greywater	Lightly contaminated water captured and reused for a second purpose, eg water from wash basins used to flush toilets.
Groundwater	Water beneath the ground's surface.
Groundwater source protection zones	Zones where there is a risk of contamination from any activities that might cause pollution in the area. The closer the activity is to the source, the greater

the risk. Used in conjunction with the groundwater protection policy to set up pollution prevention measures in areas that are at higher risk, and to monitor the activities of potential polluters nearby.

Heritage bodies

These bodies have a general duty to conserve heritage, to carry out scheduling of historic remains, and to undertake research. They comprise English Heritage, Cadw, Historic Scotland and NIEA.

Landfill tax

Introduced in October 1996, as a tax payable to HM Revenue and Customs by the operator, on all active waste materials going to landfill. Landfill tax in April 2010 is £48 per tonne for active waste, and £2.50 for inert or inactive waste. Landfill tax is currently scheduled to increase by £8 per tonne per annum, under the tax escalator. There are certain defined exemptions (see Section 4.8.10).

Local biodiversity action plan (LBAP)

Used by local authorities and others to identify ecological objectives and targets. Aimed at ensuring sustainable development in relation to processes such as planning, the LBAP helps conserve and save valuable habitats as well as plant or animal species. LBAPs link to a national biodiversity plan set by government.

Local planning authorities (LPA)

Based within local councils, the LPA is responsible for local planning issues including control of building works and development of land, protection of hedgerows and trees and listed buildings.

Mitigation

Refers to the actions and measures that may be taken to eliminate or reduce the effect of a scheme's development or operation.

Nature conservancy bodies

Countryside Council for Wales (CCW), Natural England, Scottish Natural Heritage (SNH) and NIEA have regional responsibility for promoting the conservation of wildlife and natural features.

Noise	Often explained as being a sound that is not desired. Sound is a wave motion carried by air particles between the source and the receiver (usually the ear).
Noise abatement zones	Local authorities have the power to set up a noise abatement zone as an area-based approach for controlling commercial and industrial noise.
Polluter pays principle (PPP)	Also known as extended polluter responsibility (EPR) is an environmental principle that requires that polluting parties are made liable to pay for the damages they cause to the natural environment. This principle is enforced through the Environmental Damage and Liability Regulations 2009.
Pollution	The introduction of a substance that has the potential to cause harm to the environment or any other living organisms supported by the environment. Pollutants include silty water, oils, chemicals, litter, dust and mud. Also, excessive levels of noise and light can be classed as pollution.
Prescribed processes	Any activities carried out on premises or by means of mobile plant (eg concrete crusher) capable of causing pollution to the environment. Nearly always require a local authority or Environment Agency (SEPA in Scotland) licence/permit.
Recycling	Collecting and separating materials from waste and processing them to produce useable products.
Remediation notice(s)	Having identified any contaminated land within its area, the environmental regulator or the local authority may serve on an appropriate person such a notice, specifying what needs to be done to remediate the land and the times when it should be done.
Section 60 notice	Enforcement action issued under the Control of Pollution Act 1974 by the local authority to control noise pollution and nuisance on construction sites.

If raised, the conditions must be complied with until revoked or successfully appealed against.

Section 61 consent

An agreement with the local authority issued under the Control of Pollution Act 1974 to permit activities with the potential to cause nuisance (eg noise on site to occur).

Sewerage provider

Regional wastewater utility company or Scottish Water (for Scottish residential customers) responsible for removal and treatment of foul water/sewage. Overseen by NIEA in Northern Ireland.

Stakeholders

Persons or groups who are directly or indirectly affected by a project, as well as those who may have interests in a project and/or the ability to influence its outcome, either positively or negatively.

Statutory consultees

Organisations that must be consulted at the planning stage of projects. These organisations include regulators, heritage bodies and nature conservation bodies.

Sustainable development

"Development that meets the needs of the present without compromising the ability of future generations to meet their own needs" (World Commission on Environment and Development, 1987).

Sustainable timber

Wood that is obtained from a sustainably managed forest.

Trade effluent consent

A consent that must be sought from the relevant water and sewerage company or authority before an organisation can discharge trade effluent to a public foul sewer or to a private sewer that connects to a public sewer.

Transfer note

Required under the Environmental Protection (Duty of Care) Regulations 1991 and the Controlled Waste (Duty of Care) Regulations (Northern Ireland) in Northern Ireland 2002 as a legal document describing the transfer of controlled/directive waste between duty-holders.

Transfer station Facility where waste is transferred from collection vehicles to larger vehicles or onto rail or river for onward transport for disposal. Also refers to a facility that segregates waste.

Waste Any substance or object that the holder discards, intends to discard or is required to discard:

☐ controlled waste – household, commercial and industrial waste

☐ directive waste – material that the producer or holder discards

☐ inert waste, eg clean bricks, blocks, concrete

☐ non-hazardous waste – a landfill tax classification

☐ hazardous waste – hazardous or dangerous to life or the environment (defined a special waste in Scotland).

Waste minimisation/ resource efficiency The reduction of waste at source by understanding and changing processes to minimise its production. It includes the substitution of less environmentally harmful materials in the production process.

Wildlife corridor A linear habitat, or range of habitats in which species can survive, and along which they can move to other wildlife areas. Examples include rivers and streams, hedges and shelterbelts, field and road margins.

Works notice See *Enforcement notices*.

Acronyms and abbreviations

AGL	Aggregates Levy
AONB	Area of outstanding natural beauty
ASSI	Area of special scientific interest (in Northern Ireland)
BAP	Biodiversity action plan
BDFO	Build-design-finance-operate
BIS	Department for Business, Innovation and Skills
BOT	Build-operate-transfer
BPM	Best practicable means
BPN	Building Preservation Notice
BRE	Building Research Establishment
BREEAM	Building Research Establishment Environmental Assessment Method
BS	British Standard
Cadw	Welsh Historic Monuments
CAR	Controlled Activities Regulations
CBM	Cement bound material
CCS	Considerate Constructors Scheme
CCTV	Closed circuit television
CCW	Countryside Council for Wales
CD&E	Construction, demolition and excavation
CECA	Civil Engineering Contractors Association
CEEQUAL	Civil Engineering Environmental Quality Assessment and Award Scheme
CFC's	Chlorofluorocarbons
CL:AIRE	Contaminated Land: Applications In Real Environments
CLR	Contaminated land report
CoPA	Control of Pollution Act 1974
COSHH	The Control of Substances Hazardous to Health Regulations 2002

CSH	Code for Sustainable Homes
CWS	County wildlife sites
DARD	Department of Agriculture and Rural Development (Northern Ireland)
DCLG	Department of Communities and Local Government
DCMS	Department for Culture, Media and Sport
dB	Decibel
D&B	Design and build
Defra	Department of Environment Food and Rural Affairs
DOENI	Department of the Environment Northern Ireland
DQRA	Detailed quantitative risk assessment
DREAM	Defence Realm Environmental Assessment Methodology
DRI	Demolition recovery index
EHO	Environmental health officer
EIA	Environmental impact assessment
EMP	Environmental management plan
EMS	Environmental management system
EnCams	Environmental Campaigns
EPA	Environmental Protection Act 1990
EP	Environmental permit
EPR	Extended polluter responsibility
ES	Environmental statement
EWC	European Waste Catalogue
FBA	Furnace bottom ash
FSC	Forest Stewardship Council
GHG	Greenhouse gas
HSE	Health and Safety Executive
HVAC	Heating, ventilating and air conditioning

Acronyms and abbreviations

IBA	Incinerator bottom ash
ICE	Institution of Civil Engineers
IFA	Institute of Field Archaeologists
ISO	International Standards Organisation
KPH	Kier Partnership Homes
KPI	Key performance indicator
LBAP	Local biodiversity action plan
LEED	Leadership in Energy and Environmental Design
LNR	Local nature reserve
LPA	Local planning authority
MCerts	Monitoring Certification Scheme
MDF	Medium density fibreboard
MPS	Minerals Policy Statement (England)
MRF	Material recovery facility
MS	Method statement(s)
NIEA	Northern Ireland Environment Agency
NNR	National nature reserve
NRSWA	New Roads and Street Works Act 1991
PAN	Planning Advice Note (Scotland)
PEFC	Programme for Endorsement of Forest Certification
PFA	Pulverised fuel ash
PFI	Private Finance Initiative
PLCs	Permits, licenses and consents
PPC	Pollution Prevention & Control
PPE	Personal protective equipment
PPG	Pollution Prevention Guidelines
PPP	Polluter pays principle
PVC	Polyvinyl chloride
RA	Recycled aggregate

RAMSAR	Wetlands of international importance
RAP	Recycled asphalt planings
RCA	Recycled concrete aggregate
REACH	Registration, Evaluation, Authorisation and Restriction of Chemicals
RIGS	Regionally important geological sites
RSPB	Royal Society for the Protection of Birds
SAC	Special areas of conservation
SEA	Strategic environmental assessment
SEPA	Scottish Environment Protection Agency
SINC	Site of importance for nature conservation
SLAM	Single living accommodation modernisation
SMC	Scheduled monument consent
SNCI	Sites of nature conservation interest
SNCO	Statutory Nature Conversation Organisation
SNH	Scottish Natural Heritage
SPA	Special protection area
SSSI	Sites of special scientific interest
SuDS	Sustainable drainage systems
SWMP	Site waste management plan
TMP	Traffic management plan
TPO	Tree Preservation Order
UEA	University of East Anglia
UKCG	UK Contractors Group
WAC	Waste acceptance criteria
WAP	Waste acceptance procedures
WHS	World Heritage Site
WRAP	Waste and Resources Action Programme
WWF	World Wildlife Fund

Construction can impact on the environment but, with careful management, potential negative impacts (eg excess noise and water, air and ground pollution) can be avoided or minimised. There are many benefits that can be gained from good environmental management of construction projects. There are many legal and other obligations that must be complied with.

Increasingly, efforts are being made within the construction industry to improve the environment:

- [ ] government and regulators are requiring increasingly high standards of environmental management from industry
- [ ] clients are requesting evidence of environmental credentials from contractors before awarding contracts
- [ ] contractors are assisting their suppliers and subcontractors to manage and improve the environmental performance of their own operations
- [ ] top level commitment is demonstrated by environmental policies
- [ ] many construction companies have an environmental management system (EMS) (see Section 2.1.7) and report on environmental and sustainability issues
- [ ] on-site personnel are adopting many environmental initiatives.

There are many incentives for improving performance, which include:

- [ ] improved environmental conditions resulting from good practice
- [ ] effective risk management to avoid the cost implications of failing to meet environmental obligations, regulations and legislation
- [ ] cleaner and safer site conditions
- [ ] resource efficiency to maximise achievable cost savings
- [ ] demonstrating benefits of good environmental performance to interested parties including clients, regulators and the public
- [ ] creating a better place for people to live in.

1.1 Sustainable construction

"Sustainability" and "sustainable development" are terms defined differently by different people. The original definition of sustainable development (and the one still most widely used), was made in the

Bruntland Report (World Commission on Environment and Development, 1987), which defined it as:

> *"Development that meets the needs of the present without compromising the ability of future generations to meet their own needs".*

Sustainable development is crucial to the development of the UK and is a principle at the highest level of national planning.

In June 2008 the UK Government released the Strategy for Sustainable Construction (HM Government, 2008). The strategy aims to achieve sustainable construction by:

☐ providing clarity to business on the government's position by bringing together diverse regulations and initiatives relating to sustainability

☐ setting and committing to higher standards to help work towards sustainability in specific areas

☐ making specific commitments by industry and the Government to adopt sustainable construction.

A progress report was published in September 2009.

This guide is largely focused on environmental good practice, but also considers economic and social aspects of sustainable development. The adoption of good practices in relation to environmental management can deliver several benefits through sustainable development.

Environmental benefits

☐ reduced damage to the surrounding air, water resources, land and to fauna and flora from potentially damaging activities

☐ reduced demand for resources through better material selection, procurement and management, less waste and greater use of recycled, reclaimed and sustainably sourced materials

☐ improvement of the local environment by identifying opportunities to increase biodiversity

☐ reduced greenhouse gas (GHG) emissions by adoption of sustainable procurement principles and monitoring of resource use on site.

Social benefits

☐ reduced nuisance to neighbours by liaising with the local community before and during the project to keep them informed about works that could affect them

☐ increased knowledge/skills for site workers learning and adopting good practices

☐ improved environmental profile by establishing good relationships with environmental regulators and the local authority.

Economic benefits

☐ improved opportunities to tender through demonstration of sound environmental performance and effective risk management

☐ less money wasted on fines for non-compliance with legislation and associated costs of clean-up, legal fees and management time

☐ fewer delays to the project by fully characterising the site before works start, reducing costs incurred by delayed surveys

☐ better cost certainty through improved materials resource management

☐ cost savings through improved energy efficiency and carbon management.

Benefits are felt at both a corporate and a project level. So what do they mean to the individual?

☐ site managers can demonstrate better spend control

☐ site engineer's workload can be reduced by fewer conflicts

☐ risk of complaints can be reduced

☐ likelihood of negative press locally can be reduced

☐ avoiding delays is more likely

☐ improved employee motivation on site.

1.2   Environmental obligations

There are many controls that ensure good practice is followed. These have both legislative and contractual origins and include:

Employer/client requirements

Contract conditions between client and developer can allow businesses to define the environmental standards that will be achieved on site during construction. They provide the opportunity to, for example, set targets, specify site waste management protocols, define scheme improvements, eg working as a "considerate contractor", improve biodiversity and get buy-in from subcontractors. Employer/client requirements and planning conditions together form specific contractual conditions.

National environmental protection legislation

It is enforced primarily by the environmental regulators to protect both the natural environment and residents around sites. Legislation (eg the Environment Act 1995) is in place to protect specific features of the environment; with sites being designated and protected by virtue of their ecological, archaeological, geological or geomorphological importance.

Court convictions can lead to unlimited fines for a company and/or imprisonment or community service for the person (individual and/or appropriate director or senior manager) responsible. Liability will be more probable if it is found that suitable training, procedures or equipment were not being provided. Environmental convictions can preclude companies from tenders/frameworks and can mean environmental permits being refused.

Local control

Local authorities can impose several requirements through the powers given to them by national legislation including noise and air controls. Planning legislation at both a local and national level is the main control on construction development covering many aspects including scale and traffic. Other government funded bodies such as the Environment Agency, Natural England, SEPA, and NIEA can also impose local controls.

Planning conditions can be imposed on a project through the planning system, such as Section 106 agreements of the Town and Country Planning

Act 1990 (legal agreements between planning department and developer that cannot be appealed against) to ensure the commitments made to the local communities are delivered, and may include provisions made after an environmental assessment.

Corporate control

Many contractors have corporate environmental policies and an EMS that employees are required to follow. There may be a specific site environmental management plan (EMP) for a project that stipulates controls to minimise environmental damage. Other corporate controls include:

☐ company targets and objectives set through the EMS

☐ key performance indicators (KPIs)

☐ company action plans

☐ a sustainability policy

☐ signing up to external initiatives (eg 2012 commitment).

2.1 The management framework

This section outlines a framework for managing the environment on site. Steps 1 to 5 should be followed for every site.

2.1.1 Setting the scene

Effective environmental management on site requires a team effort. This includes inputs from the main contractor and subcontractors (on site), the contractors' organisation (off site), designers, clients, customer and suppliers. To manage this teamwork effectively the site manager (and the managers of subcontractors) should follow these steps:

STEP 1   Identify the environmental obligations of the project

☐   identify legal and other obligations (eg requirement achieve an assessment scheme, ie CEEQUAL of BREEAM (see Section 2.5)

☐   identify environmental requirements contained in the project brief, specification or contract documents

☐   consult with the relevant regulator(s) – be proactive to give the regulator an opportunity to identify and address issues at an early planning stages

This step should include a review of any EIA, environmental statement (ES) (including actions required within any environmental action plan produced) or other client/designer derived assessment.

STEP 2   Identify the environmental risks (including potential emergencies) particular to the site

☐   review relevant documentation identified in Step 1 (see Section 1.2)

☐   talk to environmental regulators about their concerns for the site at an early stage

☐   liaise with clients and designers to establish how they can help identify and overcome potential environmental difficulties (see Section 2.1.6)

☐   compile an environmental risk register for the site (ie assess the environmental risks)

☐   during site induction, alert all site personnel to the risks associated with the construction on site

☐   discuss and agree potential pollution incident management procedure(s).

It is important that any queries are resolved at an early stage to avoid misunderstandings and problems during construction.

STEP 3   Identify environmental responsibilities

☐ define the environmental responsibilities of all personnel on site, including those who are involved in implementing and monitoring initiatives (see Section 2.1.3)

☐ define lines of communication between site personnel, and those responsible for producing the site environmental plan (see *Key message*).

The principle contractor must ensure that the environmental responsibilities of subcontractors or others working on behalf of the organisation are clearly defined and communicated.

March

The better responsibilities are defined and understood the more likely they are to be adopted.

STEP 4   Establish an environmental management plan (EMP)

☐ information gathered in Steps 1 to 3 can be used to form the basis of the EMP

☐ the most important features of an EMP are that it is site specific, accessible, regularly revised and in constant use

☐ the site EMP can be used to develop method statements (MS) for specific components of work

☐ MS are important documents on site as these will be referenced during the process and will incorporate not only environmental, but also all other requirements, eg health and safety and buildability. If work is in an area of environmental importance/significance or in, near to or liable to affect water the regulator should be consulted before the start of any works to agree the MS. This may form part of planning conditions

☐ a site waste management plan (SWMP) must be developed as part of the site EMP

☐   Section 2.1.7 outlines how the site EMP can fit into the environmental management system of the company.

STEP 5   Monitoring and follow up

☐   a robust monitoring system should be implemented to ensure the requirements of the EMP are met, eg weekly site environmental checklists, highlighting any issues, and describing actions taken

☐   all monitoring data should be retained so there is an auditable trail. Monitoring refers to a wide range of activities, including:

     ☐   SWMP data

     ☐   audit reports

     ☐   maintaining and reviewing training records

     ☐   chemical analysis of discharges and/or baseline levels and nearby streams

     ☐   waste transfer or consignment notes

     ☐   records of dust generation

     ☐   noise monitoring records.

☐   measures should be in place to rectify any non-compliance with the EMP that is raised during monitoring

☐   monitoring will provide baseline data, which can be used for setting objectives and targets.

2.1.2   Working with regulators

Whatever the size of the project it will be necessary to work with regulators. Early interaction with them is important for a successful relationship. Regulators have a diverse range of specific responsibilities and powers to enforce legislation. Some of their main responsibilities are included in Table 2.1.

Table 2.1
Regulatory categories and their core responsibilities

Regulator	Responsibilities
Local authority	Noise, air quality, traffic, the planning process and contaminated land
Environmental regulators	Discharges to land and water, waste, water abstraction, ground and water contamination, engineering activities in or near waters, nature conservation and built heritage
Nature conservation organisations	Designated ecological sites, geological and geomorphological sites and protected species
Heritage bodies	Designated archaeological and heritage sites
County archaeologist	Designated archaeological and heritage sites
Health and Safety Executive (HSE)	Health and safety including vibration and asbestos
Water and sewerage provider	Effluent discharge to public sewer

Full contact details for and responsibilities of key national regulators and heritage bodies are given in Appendix A1.

Environmental regulators should be contacted as early in the project as possible. This can help to identify the required consents and licenses, to agree on project requirements, and to minimise project delays. This is particularly relevant on projects where an environmental statement has not been produced, and is often required even when an environment statement is available.

It is important to understand and manage any planning conditions and associated guidance developed from the granting of planning permission or the equivalent requirements associated with other consents granted. This should be done by involving the planning authorities from the design phase through to completion.

It is equally important to develop a constructive dialogue with regulators to ensure they are aware of what is happening on the project and why.

Dealing with regulators	
Plan ahead and give regulators advance warning of potential problems	
Give regulators the time they need to process the enquiry, particularly when applying for permits/licences/consents	
Always display the relevant emergency number (see Appendix A1 for contact details)	
Ensure site personnel know the correct procedures for reporting incidents	
Always notify the environmental regulator of any pollution incidents or other environmental damage	

2.1.3   Environmental responsibilities

Environmental good practice on site should start with a commitment from company executives. Everyone on site is responsible for ensuring that their actions constitute good practice. Certain individuals have clearly defined roles and responsibilities as detailed in the following table, which is not an exhaustive list and it is likely that levels of responsibilities will vary within companies (see Table 2.2).

Table 2.2
Roles and responsibilities

Individual	Role
All site personnel	All individuals should follow good practice and are responsible for carrying out their activities without detrimental effects on the environment All staff should comply with systems of work including the EMP, MS and risk assessments and should carry out tasks in accordance with their training Individuals are responsible for reporting any environmental concerns and incidents to their supervisors, including suggestions for improvements
Site engineers/ foremen	Should understand the project environmental obligations and the practical measures needed to comply with them They should ensure that the control measures identified (EMP, MS etc) are effectively carried out Identify the need for and deliver regular toolbox talks
Site manager	Principal responsibility for environmental management on site by ensuring: ☐ all measures in the EMP, including consents, are implemented on site. This includes ensuring that adequate resources are allocated to environmental management on site ☐ environmental issues in MS/risk assessments are effectively communicated on site and that appropriate training (including induction) is delivered ☐ regular environmental inspections are carried out ☐ environmental instructions from the client are carried out The manager should liaise with all appropriate stakeholders, including regulators
Environmental co-ordinator/ advisor	Carrying out environmental duties including producing documentation, liaison with third parties, carrying out inspections and audits, delivering environmental training and toolbox talks etc
Designer	Responsible for ensuring that environmental aspects are considered and incorporated into the design as appropriate, and that all residual issues or impacts are communicated to the client/principal contractor

Table 2.2 (contd)
Roles and responsibilities

Individual	Role
Middle management	Provide corporate advice on environmental legislation, good practice and company environmental policy, and translate decisions into action at site level. They should review training needs and arrange for it to be provided
Director with responsibility for the environment/executive board	Responsible for: □ overall environmental governance and strategy □ company legislative compliance □ development of the environmental policy □ ensuring that environmental aspects are delivered for all projects □ ensuring adequate resources are allocated to achieve the environmental standards set out by the company
Client	Responsible for ensuring that all relevant environmental documentation and information eg existing consents, is communicated to the designer and contractor Also responsible for setting the standard for environmental management on site, which is set out in the contracts

Successful environmental management relies on communication. It is crucial that everyone is aware of the key issues, has the relevant information to deal with them, understands their responsibilities, and provides feedback to those in charge.

2.1.4   Subcontractor responsibilities and the supply chain

Subcontractors and those further down the supply chain need to understand their environmental obligations and ensure they meet them. As with any controls, environmental responsibility can be implemented through incentives and/or penalties. It is important for contractors and subcontractors to work together to ensure successful delivery of projects. The following checklist provides suggestions on selecting and managing subcontractors:

Selecting and managing subcontractors	
Subcontractors should present proof of their past environmental performance along with records of past and pending prosecutions	
Ensure that subcontractors sign up to the implementation of the site EMP and SWMP before starting work	
Ensure subcontractors attend environmental training sessions/inductions	
Ensure subcontractors are aware of their environmental obligations on the project	
The contract should include requirements to follow good environmental practice	
Audit the performance of subcontractors during the project	

2.1.5   Raising awareness

It is important to raise awareness of environmental issues so that people on site know what environmental good practice is and know where to obtain information. Many contractors, particularly on large projects, employ both an environmental advisor/consultant who is able to collaborate with regulators and site personnel/managers who ensure good practice is pursued throughout the duration of construction.

Training should be used on site to disseminate good practice guidance relevant to a particular project. For a training programme to be successful, it is vital to:

☐   select a trainer with appropriate knowledge, skills and experience (often peer-level training is most effective)

- ☐ make training specific to the audience
- ☐ ensure training is engaging and relevant
- ☐ follow up and refresh training to keep abreast of changes in legislation and codes of practice
- ☐ maintain records of all training undertaken/planned.

Key aspects of training for site managers and engineers should include:

- ☐ waste management
- ☐ emergency procedures for environmental incidents
- ☐ choice of plant, plant maintenance and safe refuelling
- ☐ consent management monitoring requirements
- ☐ choice of working methods
- ☐ practical actions to ensure compliance with relevant legislation
- ☐ importance of good housekeeping
- ☐ sources of advice
- ☐ personal responsibility/liability.

All site personnel should be given a site induction including basic environmental issues/concerns. Further training such as spill kit use (see Figure 2.1) should be given to all relevant site personnel. For training to be effective, adequate time should be set aside to inform people about the issues that are relevant to the site and work.

Figure 2.1
*Spill response training
(courtesy Galliford Try)*

Toolbox talks should be carried out on a regular basis on aspects appropriate to the construction works. Copies of those produced by Civil Engineering Contractors Association (CECA) and the UK Contractors Group (UKCG) and are available from <www.ceca.co.uk> and <www.ukcg.org.uk> respectively.

Further on-site training guidance is available from several bodies including CIRIA and environmental regulators.

2.1.6   Client and designer responsibilities

Designers should consider the environmental impact of their designs by conducting an environmental risk assessment. If the design of temporary or permanent works compromises environmental good practice, the designer should be informed.

Where the contract imposes environmental constraints it is worth discussing the reasons with the designers and/or client. It may be possible to explore alternative approaches that have less impact (eg using recycled or secondary aggregate, and heating, ventilating and air conditioning (HVAC) systems).

2.1.7 Environmental management systems (EMS)

An EMS takes a systematic approach to assessing, managing and monitoring the environmental impacts of a project. This includes the definition of management responsibilities and development of documented procedures.

The main international standard for EMS used in the UK is ISO 14001.

BS 8555 provides guidance on the phased implementation of an EMS to ISO 14001. CIRIA has produced a CD-Rom on adopting BS 8555 (Hall and Burr, 2007), which provides guidance and templates for construction companies wishing to achieve ISO 14001.

2.2 Planning, setting up and managing the site

This section outlines measures that should be considered when setting up and managing the site to achieve environmental good practice.

2.2.1 Enabling works

Liaison with the regulator

Regulators encourage contractors to take a proactive approach regarding environmental management on site, so it is important to involve them from an early stage in the project.

Site survey

Before any works begin, a survey needs to be carried out (if an EIA is undertaken these surveys will be undertaken as part of the EIA process). It is useful to contact the appropriate regulator at this stage as they can provide advice on potential sensitive areas and, if necessary, on possible mitigation options.

Surveys are divided into three phases

1   **Desk-based indicative survey**

    The first stage should be a desk-based study reviewing drawings/plans and contract information, supported by environmental risk registers and the company's EMS. If the company does not operate an EMS or have environmental risk registers, this stage should still be completed.

The desk-based survey is a process of identifying where activities may have a positive or negative impact on the environment on and around the site. Any feature, habitat, area or living organism that can potentially be negatively impacted can be termed an environmental receptor.

Details of all receptors identified should be recorded and be cross referenced against site activities that are likely to affect them, for example scrubland would be affected by clearance/set-up removing vegetation across the site.

2 Site walk through

The second stage should be a walk through by site management, preferably with an environmental manager/advisor or site representative with environmental training. This is to follow up the items recorded from the desk-based survey, reviews of drawings and site maps and those identified in contract requirements etc. On-site reviews will help to define appropriate action to control potential impacts on receptors. Also, the walk through will help decide where further assistance and/or technical surveys are needed. Also other receptors not previously identified, such as trees with nesting birds or potential bat roosts, drains not marked on site plans, or potentially contaminated ground, may be discovered.

3 Technical surveys

A collective term for surveys that should be conducted by a suitably qualified professional, such as noise, ecology and contaminated land surveys etc. Although it is good practice for site management to identify environmental receptors, these will need to be investigated further. This will benefit the site as technically competent persons conducting surveys will be able to propose mitigation when agreeing working measures with regulators.

The first stage should be a desk-study based on drawings/plans and contract information or online databases, for example Magic <**www.magic.gov.uk**> for ecology, to identify any potential environmental risks.

The second stage is a site survey to confirm the findings of the first stage, the survey should be undertaken by environmental specialists, eg a trained ecologist. If a site survey highlights risks to be avoided that have not been managed at the design stage it should be sent to the designers for re-consideration.

It is important to survey a site early in the construction process to allow enough lead in time to avoid or mitigate any potential effects.

In addition to identifying potential impacts, ecology surveys may provide an opportunity to improve the ecological value of the site during the contract and add to the biodiversity of the area. Refer to local biodiversity action plans (LBAPs) developed by the local authority. These can provide useful details of national and local sensitive flora, fauna and habitat types that will provide opportunities for improvement as well as helping to identify potential effects on receptors.

Site clearance

It is important to plan the site clearance at the appropriate time of year, to avoid disruption to wildlife and to comply with the associated legislation that protects various species during certain seasons (see Table 4.1).

2.2.2   Site offices

When planning the site layout, contractors' offices and equipment should be sited to minimise pollution and other forms of disturbance to surrounding neighbours. Also, site offices need to be located so as not to cause any environmental harm (eg destruction of ecological habitats). Hedges or existing trees can be used to screen sites and compounds in rural areas. In urban areas the construction works are usually screened with suitable hoarding (see Figure 2.2) or acoustic screens.

Figure 2.2
Site hoarding – Jarrow
(courtesy TT2 Ltd)

There are many general environmental issues relating to the internal office environment including energy use, waste (eg paper use, toner cartridge) and the use of electrical equipment to consider.

Carbon management and energy efficiency are important considerations for the entire construction process and the Strategy for Sustainable Construction contains a target of reducing construction based carbon by 15 per cent by 2012 (BIS, 2009). Site offices have been identified as important contributors to carbon emissions from the construction process and should be assessed on their energy performance.

The Strategic Forum for Construction has published an action plan to reduce carbon emissions in the construction sector as well as producing a baseline for carbon emissions from construction sites (Strategic Forum for Construction, 2010). Carbon Construct <**www.carbonconstruct.com**> provides a summary of key initiatives relating to carbon across the construction and related sectors.

STRATEGIC FORUM FOR CONSTRUCTION (2010)
Carbon: Reducing the footprint of the construction process. An action plan to reduce carbon emissions
Report 006, prepared by Joan Ko on behalf of the Strategic Forum for Construction and the Carbon Trust. Available to download from <www.strategicforum.org.uk/> or <www.constructionproducts.org.uk/publications/page.aspx?Id=504>

2.2.3   Site management

Most pollution incidents, environmental damage or other causes of complaints can be avoided through careful planning, training and communication of environmental issues on site. Most measures needed to prevent pollution are inexpensive, especially if they are included at the planning stage. In contrast, the costs of cleaning up a pollution incident or repairing (restoring) environmental damage can be very high, as can abatement measures put in place as a response to complaints.

Also, pollution prevention and waste minimisation measures may offer substantial economic benefits. These include reducing the need for expensive raw materials, fewer site accidents and a reduced risk of prosecution for environmental offences. Introduction of pollution prevention measures is the first step, but for these to be effective, managers should be committed and employees should understand why they are needed and be suitably trained.

The following checklist details steps to be taken in managing a site, but is not exhaustive as some sites will have their own unique issues that need to be appropriately managed.

Site management

Define environmental responsibilities	
Establish contact with appropriate regulators	
Ensure everyone on site is aware of their responsibilities and liabilities	
Through a site induction, make everyone aware of the project environmental issues and environmental standards	
Site personnel need to be aware of spill or other contamination response procedures and storage requirements	
Engage and inform any neighbours of works to be undertaken	
Adequately protect site against vandalism, theft and breakage	
Ensure all consents/licences/permits have been obtained before any activities controlled by them is carried out (eg water discharge from site)	
A drainage plan identifying foul and surface water drainage needs to be accessible	
Identify nearby rivers, streams or groundwater etc and ensure they are inspected regularly	
Identify restricted areas for archaeology, ecology, soil storage	
Mark drains appropriately to distinguish them	
Provide fuel bunds and/or internally bunded tanks	
Provide a waste storage area	
Designate concrete wash out area	
Wheel wash or road cleaning equipment should be provided	
Indicate all designated haul routes	
Display environmental awareness posters/bulletins	
Display warning signs on site prominently	
The company environmental policy should be available for reference	

One example of an on-site activity requiring careful management is that of road sweeper arisings generated by keeping site access routes clean. These arisings could contain fuel residues, road salt and other substances that may harm the environment. As part of the sites duty of care they are required to be discharged at an authorised facility if they are not this could result in prosecution. Where, due to logistical issues or overnight working, this is not possible, the environmental regulator should be contacted to discuss viable alternatives.

2.2.4 Procuring and managing materials (including plant)

Considering the environmental impact during the procurement of materials has many benefits for the site (see Section 4.5.2). It is advisable to establish a procurement strategy that can be applied on each site. Such a strategy should consider:

- [ ] substituting virgin materials for those with recycled content
- [ ] substituting hazardous materials for non-hazardous alternatives (less pollution potential, safer to use for employees, easier and cheaper disposal)
- [ ] ensuring ethical sourcing of materials and products
- [ ] considering origin and transport of products (what are the environmental benefits of locally sourced goods, over goods sourced from another continent?)
- [ ] the embodied energy, CO_2 and water of materials when selecting products (as part of assessing the whole-life impact of the project).

Making changes to procurement to incorporate such suggestions may not be a simple task, so developing a strategy that can be applied on more than one project will allow continued improvement. Selection of materials is critical and so forms a significant part of environmental and sustainability assessment schemes on projects (see Section 2.5).

Managing materials

Improving the management of materials and components has environmental benefits through increased resource and site efficiency. Where site personnel follow established procedures for managing materials and components (see Section 4.5.5) there will be fewer incidents of spillages and contamination arising from incorrect storage or handling, and less damage to materials and components. This means less waste of raw materials (see Section 4.5.4). The introduction of SWMP means that site personnel should be aware of and plan for the management, storage and disposal of materials that come on site in advance. This requires well planned ordering and management of materials. Also, good housekeeping on site will ensure good storage and less waste.

Ordering and receiving deliveries

Develop a procurement strategy that considers the environmental life cycle of materials	
Seek to reduce use of hazardous materials	
Seek to use more materials with recycled content	
Ensure the identified storage area is on impermeable base and within containment to prevent spills/leaks	
Order the correct quantity of materials to arrive when they are needed to reduce the required storage time and risk of damage and theft	
Find out in what form materials will be delivered, so that the appropriate unloading plant can be arranged and space set aside	
Ensure deliveries are received by a member of site personnel who is able to carry out a quality inspection to avoid wastage	
Select packaging materials for deliveries that can assist effective/secure storage and movement of materials on site. Seek packaging take back schemes with suppliers	
Arrange "take back" schemes for excess materials	
Avoid sensitive times for deliveries, eg rush hour, school run	

Storage

It is important to manage storage areas on site efficiently to reduce the risk of damage, injury to site personnel and theft. When storing materials keep the following points in mind:

☐   ensure that the suppliers' instructions are being followed

☐   plan the storage area so that frequently used items are easy to access

☐   store valuable materials, or those that are hazardous or attractive to thieves, in a secure area, out of sight of the public

☐ store materials away from waste storage containers and from vehicle movements that could cause accidental damage

☐ secure lightweight materials to protect them from wind damage or loss

☐ take special care over the storage of materials that are potentially polluting (see Section 4.5.5)

☐ storage and use of perishable items (eg bags of cement) should follow the "first in first out" rule.

Handling

Handling of materials on site should be kept to a minimum to avoid the risk of damage and/or injury to site personnel. Materials should be handled using only the appropriate apparatus including cranes, trucks, fork lifts and even manual handling, ensuring that the suppliers' instructions on their operation are always followed.

Reuse of materials on site

Be aware of the potential to reuse existing materials on site, for example:

☐ potentially valuable construction products that could be salvaged from existing buildings

☐ using excavated soils (this may be subject to a waste management licensing/environmental permitting exemption) and other materials, on other areas of the site (eg for raising ground level or for general landscaping)

☐ stockpiles of soil or other organic materials that could result in contaminated runoff into watercourses etc should be stabilised immediately by covering them with appropriate sheeting or seeding with fast growing vegetation

☐ reusing pallets delivered to the site in temporary works

☐ reusing left over materials of products from other areas of the site (possibly through a site warehouse)

☐ reusing hardcore, planing and waste concrete, eg for landscaping or footpaths

☐ ensure good housekeeping.

2.2.5 Traffic and access routes

It is important to manage site traffic because it can cause delays to local traffic and create a safety hazard both on and off site. Often, common sources of complaint are the emissions, noise and visual intrusion of queuing vehicles.

Access routes

The use of public roads for site access may be restricted in terms of:

☐ vehicle weight and width

☐ time restrictions

☐ parking

☐ minimising pedestrian conflict

☐ low-headroom (eg low bridge).

Consultation with the local police and local highway authority to address these issues and effectively manage them should occur before works begin. A traffic management plan should be devised and incorporated into the site management plan (see Section 4.7.2).

Managing site traffic

Plan the timing of deliveries to avoid vehicles waiting. Where several deliveries are likely to take place over a short period, designate a waiting area some distance from the site and call in deliveries when access is clear.

Arrange suitable designated car parking areas for site personnel to reduce public inconvenience. Consider using a park-and-ride or car-share scheme. The Department for Transport has produced guidance on travel plans (see <**www.dft.gov.uk/pgr/sustainable/travelplans**>). Free help with developing a travel plan is available via <**www.travelplans.org.uk**>.

Often, construction sites are blamed for disturbance caused by vehicles that are not associated with the site. To avoid this, give the main contractor and regular delivery vehicles visible identifying marks.

Managing site traffic

Develop a traffic management plan	
Designate an area of the site for site personnel's vehicles	
Put procedures in place to prevent delivery vehicles from queuing outside the site boundary	
Make delivery drivers aware of traffic restrictions on and around the site	
Inspect vehicles regularly for leaks	
Delivery vehicle engines should be turned off while waiting to be unloaded	
Vehicles should be loaded and unloaded off the highway wherever possible	
Provide wheel washing facilities to avoid the spread of mud onto public highways, if this is not possible arrange for a road sweeper to regularly clear the road	

2.2.6   Site clearance following completion

This is a phase of the works that usually receives little attention, but it can cause a number of problems. In clearing the site it is vital that wastes are managed in accordance with regulations (see Section 4.8.6), including avoiding burning of any clearance materials. Before a project is considered to be complete, the contractor is required to clear away, and remove from the site, all equipment and materials including:

- [ ] plant
- [ ] surplus materials
- [ ] waste and skips
- [ ] rubbish
- [ ] residues
- [ ] signage
- [ ] cabins
- [ ] temporary works.

Case study 2.1
Benefits of early environmental management
planning (courtesy Morrison Construction)

A flood defence scheme located in a densely populated area. The site was located between two residential tower blocks, next to a sensitive watercourse and reedbed containing protected species. The work involved piling, brick work, excavation and fill operations, and transportation of materials. The scheme benefited from early involvement of company environmental specialists, as follows:

☐ noise, vibration, nuisance, contaminated land, ecology were identified as key issues on the environmental constraints plan, which was produced and communicated before the work on site

☐ a Section 61 consent was submitted and accepted by the council detailing the companies' construction activities and proposed methods of mitigation

☐ a letter drop produced by the site team was handed out to all residents. Communication was maintained through local residents groups to indicate when changes were expected such as asking for parked cars to be temporarily moved from the access road while the piles were delivered to site

☐ the sensitive ecology resulted in barriers being erected to prevent material from works falling into these areas

☐ land contamination was identified as a potential risk and communicated to a site team through toolbox talks. When contamination was found, containment was put in place to ensure no risk to operatives and members of the public. Waste was recycled instead of going to landfill wherever practicable. The framework environmental advisor was kept involved in this process from early identification, through to contaminant and removal from site

☐ because of early and continued involvement, no complaints were received from the residents regarding the work. Also, no environmental incident resulted from the activities, the Environment Agency as the client was impressed with the environmental standards achieved, and special praise was received from the noise team at the local council who were delighted with the excellent standard of work.

2.3   Interaction with the local community

2.3.1   Communication and community relations

Developing effective communication and consultation with the local community is important to minimise the likelihood of causing a nuisance (eg noise, dust, waste). Such communication should be initiated at the start of the project and continued throughout. Techniques to do this include letter drops, newspaper articles and meetings.

If the community is aware of what is happening complaints will be minimal. Be prepared to explain the project and to answer questions. Do not deviate from the company or client commitments, or agree additional measures. Use it as an opportunity to listen and reassure.

Public consultation is particularly important when operations that cause disturbance are being carried out for a significant period of time. Try to explain the efforts that are being made to limit the impacts of operations by phasing and other control measures. When considering how to liaise with the local community, follow the steps in the checklist here:

Liaising with local community
Note: some points are only appropriate to large sites

Identify and keep informed key local community representatives, such as parish councillors and residents representatives	
Visit occupants of sensitive buildings (such as schools, nursing homes and hospitals) and keep them informed of progress	
Prepare a leaflet and distribute it to nearby residents or occupiers. Provide updates or regular contributions to existing community newsletters	
Engage with the local community by working with schools and charities	
Write articles about the progress on site for the local media	
Display a "contact board" at the site perimeter so that the public know who to contact if they have a complaint or a comment. Use this board to display information on project phasing and other relevant matters	
Join the Considerate Constructors Scheme (CCS) (see Section 2.5)	
Establish a complaint line and call it to ensure that it works	
Deal quickly with any complaints that arise and in accordance with a defined complaints procedure. Create a log of complaints. Make sure all complaints are properly followed up and resolved	
Issue workers with contact cards to give to the public if approached to ensure complaints/queries are dealt with effectively	

Case study 2.2
Engagement with nearby sensitive receptors

On a particularly controversial road construction site, the site manager used contact with local schools as one of the site's initiatives to keep the community informed about the scheme. A detailed information pack was prepared for each of the local schools to use as a teaching aid.

Site personnel off-site

Good community relations can be quickly undone by the actions of site personnel when off-site. Ensure that all personnel know what is expected of them. Causes of annoyance to the community can include:

- noise on arriving or leaving site
- too many site personnel in local shops and pubs
- offensive language and behaviour
- vehicle parking
- parking on residential streets
- leaving vehicles running
- playing loud radios.

Good housekeeping

Good housekeeping is an important part of good environmental practice and it helps everyone to maintain a more efficient and safer site. The site should be tidy, secure, and have clear access routes that are well signposted. The appearance of a tidy, well-managed site can reduce the likelihood of theft, vandalism or complaints.

Good housekeeping

Segregate different types of waste as it is produced and arrange frequent removal	
Keep the site tidy and clean – a tidy site is a safe site	
Ensure that no wind-blown litter or debris leaves the site, consider covered skips to prevent wind blown litter	
Ensure that material and plant storage areas are properly managed. Cover lightweight materials with sheeting if necessary	
Keep hoardings tidy – repair and repaint when necessary, removing any fly posting or graffiti	
Frequently brush-clean the wheel washing facilities	
Keep haul routes clean	
Keep roads free from mud by using a road sweeper	
Ensure site is secure	

Working hours

Site working hours can create considerable concern and annoyance among neighbours. On some projects, working hours for noisy operations are defined by the contract documents or by local authorities – perhaps through a Section 60 notice or Section 61 agreement (see Section 4.6.4). This route should be followed early in the project to reduce the likelihood of delays and complaints being made to the local authority.

There may be opportunities for extending working hours in consultation with the local authority, but their effect on neighbours should be considered carefully – try to restrict working to sociable hours. When extended working is needed, it is important to inform neighbours in advance of the reasons for the work and its duration. Do not assume that the community's preference is for normal working hours as it may prefer longer working hours to reduce the overall length of time that they will be disrupted.

Ensure that activities are carefully timed within the working day. For example, in the same way that it is advisable to schedule deliveries outside of rush hour, other intrusive activities can be scheduled at less sensitive times. To understand the constraints, which will vary from site to site, it is important to understand the daily patterns of the neighbours. Some points to consider include:

□   in city centre sites night time noise may be more acceptable than daytime noise if there are no residential areas

□   avoid noisy activities during school hours (particularly during exam periods)

□   local restaurants appreciate less disturbance over lunch and dinner time

□   whether local businesses might require quieter periods during the day

□   whether weekend or night time working is especially sensitive

□   whether particularly sensitive areas (eg hospitals) are located near the site.

2.3.2   Lighting

Lighting can be an important deterrent to vandals and thieves, but it can annoy the local residents. Keep any site lighting at the minimum brightness necessary for adequate security and safety. Locate and direct the lighting so that it does not intrude on nearby properties. Remember that high levels of lighting waste both energy and money. Consider using infra-red lighting for security. Be aware of the possible presence of bat roosts, bird nesting areas for example on site and position lighting accordingly to reduce adverse impacts.

2.3.3   Site security

Many environmental offences are based on strict liability, with little or no defence available. Contractors can be held liable for environmental damage even when it is caused by vandals.

Site security is an important component of good environmental management. Often, vandals cause damage that harms the environment by:

□   opening taps on tanks containing fuel, or cutting fuel lines

- tipping out other liquids from drums and containers
- damaging/stealing raw materials
- playing on plant – damaging it and using it to cause damage
- spraying graffiti or fly posting on site hoardings
- destroying works in progress
- setting materials on fire.

Also, rural areas may suffer from vandalism and especially theft, as their remote location provides time for thieves to remove plant and equipment without disturbance. The need for a manned presence in a remote location often is as important as in an urban setting.

Help to reduce vandalism by securing the site, and moving valuable items and those prone to theft from public view. Store these goods in a locked container or storage area.

A secure site helps ensure the safety of the community, particularly children, as construction sites are dangerous places.

Suggested security measures

Site boundary

Secure the site boundary using perimeter fencing and high quality locks on gates. Solid barriers (eg hoardings) are more difficult to scale than chain link fences and prevent casual surveillance by prospective thieves	
Do not stack materials against the inside or outside of a site boundary/fence as this can provide an opportunity for vandals and thieves to scale it	

Within site

Ensure that potentially hazardous materials are well-secured. For storage containers with a capacity in excess of 200 litres it is a legal requirement to lock fuel outlets when they are not in use, and provide secondary containment for oil in storage	
Secure and immobilise plant and equipment overnight to prevent vandalism	
If the site is large or at high risk from trespassers install deterrents such as lights, warning notices, 24-hour security guards, alarm systems and CCTV	
Monitor movement of people on and off site by using site passes or swipe cards	
Position the site manager's office so that it has a good view of the site	
Inform local police about the site and seek their advice on security	
Consult the Fire Brigade for advice on storing fuel and flammable materials on site	
If the site experiences a problem such as vandalism or graffiti, ensure that appropriate clean-up/repair is undertaken promptly, to discourage further problems from occurring	

CIRIA C692

2.4   Incident preparedness and response

The likelihood of an incident can be minimised by effective planning through development of a site pollution incident response plan. The plan needs to identify the on-site risks and appropriate responses. Suitable equipment, such as spill kits, oil booms and absorbent material, should be held at appropriate locations on site. An effective pollution incident response plan relies on the following elements:

☐ effective pre-planning (eg use of drip-trays and booms)

☐ identification of receptors/pathways (eg surface water drains/river)

☐ identification and dissemination of contact numbers (see following section)

☐ definition of site personnel responsibilities

☐ appropriate site personnel training

☐ dry-running of incident scenarios – spill drills

☐ availability of suitable spill kits at appropriate locations on the site.

Further details on incident preparedness can be found in Pollution Prevention Guidance (PPG) 21.

Incident response plan

Ensure that all appropriate personnel are aware of the company's emergency procedure, that drain covers and spill kits are available, and personnel know how to use them. An incident response procedure (see Figure 2.3) should be based around the principle of:

STOP   CONTAIN   NOTIFY   CLEAN UP   INVESTIGATE

Contact details that should be readily available:

☐ list of site personnel and subcontractor offices

☐ the company's environmental representative

☐ fire brigade/police (999)

☐ environmental regulator

☐ spill clean up contractors

☐ local authority environmental health department

☐ sewerage provider

☐   equipment suppliers (skip hire for waste disposal)

☐   liquid waste disposal contractors.

STOP — CONTAIN — NOTIFY

STOP work immediately and prevent any more material spilling, eg right an oil drum, close valves

Cut any sources of ignition, eg switch off plant, extinguish cigarettes

CONTAIN the spillage using bunds of earth or sand, drip tray or spill kits contents immediately

Check the spill has not reached any nearby drains/manholes, watercourses, ponds and other sensitive areas. Bund drains/manholes to stop the substance entering the drainage system

Ensure that any contents of a spill kit that is used is replaced

NOTIFY the foreman/supervisor immediately giving the following information:

☐   whether the substance has entered the drain/watercourse or is affecting the environment
☐   substance involved
☐   location
☐   reason for incident
☐   quantity involved

SPILLAGE TYPE

MAJOR: cannot be controlled. Pollution has entered, or could enter a drain or watercourse. Report to foreman/supervisor immediately

MINOR: can be controlled. Pollution has not entered and cannot enter a drain or watercourse. Report to foreman/supervisor immediately

FOREMAN/SUPERVISOR INSTRUCTIONS

MAJOR: contain and report immediately to contact detailed below

MINOR: clean up immediately using appropriate materials (granules, pads etc)

CONTACT DETAILS

Environment Agency

Scottish Environment Protection Agency (SEPA)   **0800 80 70 60**

Northern Ireland Environment Agency (NIEA)

Write up a report of the incident to be retained in site records that should include the following:

☐   date, time and location of spillage
☐   substance(s) involved
☐   action taken to contain
☐   lessons to learn

Figure 2.3
Example incident response procedure

Responsibilities

Make sure everyone knows who is responsible for:

☐ taking charge at the scene

☐ reporting to the site manager

☐ reporting to the appropriate environmental regulators

☐ recording events as an incident record

☐ regularly checking that contents of the spill kits are complete.

Spill kits

Usually spill kits consisting of equipment to contain and absorb spills on land and water, are ideal for dealing with spillages. Obtain them from a reputable supplier and make sure they are specific to the oils and chemicals that are on site. At the start of the project it is important to assess the number and deployment of kits for quick access across site. The contents of a spill kit will depend on the project, but are likely to include:

☐ absorbent granules

☐ string

☐ floating "booms" or "sausages"

☐ PPE, ie gloves, goggles and overalls

☐ absorbent mats

☐ drain covers

☐ polythene sheeting and bags.

Spill kits should be stored in a marked bag or wheely bin in a well-signposted location. It is best to store them near to where they may be needed. Ensure that if materials from the spill kit are used that they are replaced immediately. Once equipment from a spill kit has been used it will need to be disposed of carefully. Some equipment may be hazardous waste (special waste in Scotland) and must be disposed of in accordance with Duty of Care legislation and the Hazardous Waste (England and Wales) Regulations 2005, Special Waste (Scotland) Regulations 1996 and the Hazardous Waste Regulations (Northern Ireland) 2005 in Northern Ireland.

Figure 2.4
Spill kit deployment
(courtesy Galliford Try)

Table 2.2 provides detail of the type of spill likely on construction sites and those materials that be used to deal with it. This is followed by further guidance on the products.

Table 2.2
Common site spills and mitigation actions

Potential pollutant on site or spilt	Oil only	Oil and water	Concrete/cement/ Bentonite	Aggressive chemicals	Less aggressive chemicals, eg solvents	Silt	Acids/alkalis
Type of spill kit/spill materials Note: further guidance is provided in the text following this table							
Universal/maintenance spill materials	✓	✗	✗	✗	✓	✗	✗
Hydrocarbon/oil only sorbents, eg pads, booms, pillows	✓	✓	✗	✗	✗	✗	✗
Chemical spill materials	✓	✗	✗	✓	✓	✗	✓
Neutralisers	✗	✗	✗	✓	✗	✗	✓
Bioremediation agents	✓	✓	✗	✗	✓	✗	✗
Surface cleaners/degreasers	✓	✓	✗	✗	✗	✗	✗
Sand	✓	✓	✗	✗	✗	✓	
Absorbent granules (should be suitable for substance)	✓	✗	✗	✗	✓	✗	✓
Drip trays (*should be made out of material suitable for substances to be contained)	✓	✓	✗	✓*	✓	✗	✓*
Plant nappies	✓	✓	✗	✗	✗	✗	✗
Reusable drain seals	✓	✓	✓	✗	✓	✓	✗
Bentonite drain seals	✓	✓	✓	✓	✓	✓	✓
Oil booms	✗	✓	✗	✗	✗	✗	✗
Fence booms	✗	✓	✓	✗	✗	✓	✗
Geotextile fence	✗	✗	✓	✗	✗	✓	✗
Straw bales	✗	✗	✓	✗	✗	✓	✗

Note:

Checks should be carried out with suppliers to ensure that the spill materials are appropriate for the substance.

Use of spill kit products

Universal/maintenance spill materials are designed to absorb and contain non-aggressive liquids and chemicals whether oil or water based. They are used for a wide range of liquids such as oils, coolants, paints, solvents, diesel and mild acids and alkalis. Some of these sorbent products are particularly useful for petrol spills because they stop the spill from releasing any more petrol vapours and make the spill safer. They are not suitable for use with aggressive chemicals.

Oil/hydrocarbon only spill kits only soak up oil and will float on water. They are ideal for mopping up spills on water such as lakes, rivers, ditches, oil bunds and in wet conditions. They are suitable for use with all fuels and hydrocarbons.

Bioremediation agents can sometimes break down an oil spill so that it becomes less polluting. They can be used to clean up oil spills but they should not be applied to oil spills on water without prior approval from the environmental regulator. These products may take some time to be effective, especially in cold weather. Check that the bioremediation product being bought does not contain any pollutants that could make matters worse.

Surface cleaners and degreasers can be used to clean and wash oil off hard surfaces such as yards. However, these products are polluting and the wash-off water from these activities should not be discharged to ground, groundwater or to surface water.

Chemical spill kits are designed to deal with all chemicals, including aggressive chemicals such as caustics, acids, solvents, oils and fuels.

Drip trays and plant nappies are used under static and portable plant to prevent leaks and drips contaminating the ground and/or water. Drip trays or similar should always be used during refuelling operations. Drip trays and plant nappies do not replace the requirements for implementing measures specified by oil storage regulations.

Socks are particularly useful for forming a ring around spills to act as an absorbent barrier and to absorb spill.

Pads and rolls are used to absorb spilt liquids and can be used on land or water. Also, pads can be placed into drip trays to catch leaks/drips from machinery.

Marine booms are much larger barriers than socks and there are several different types. Oil booms can be linked to provide containment – some are also absorbent. Fence booms can be used to capture silt and wet concrete spills.

Cushions have great absorption capacity. They are particularly useful where there is the greatest concentration of spill. Also, they can be placed into drip trays to catch leaks/drips from machinery.

For more information see CIRIA C649 *Control of water pollution from linear construction projects Site guide* (Murnane *et al*, 2006)

Note: If a major spill takes place that requires the use of spill kit equipment or an oil boom, contractors should immediately notify the appropriate environmental regulator about the spill. It is always good practice to inform the regulator of the incident if in any doubt of the potential damage caused by a spill. This alerts the regulator to the spill incident in the event a third party makes a complaint of pollution and provides the regulator with details to assess if they need to visit the site.

2   General site management issues

March

If working close to a river or similar surface water body, plan for emergencies by attaching the boom to a chain submerged across the river bed that can quickly be used to pull the boom into place in the event of a pollution incident. Also, it is important to note that booms need to be long enough to stretch over the river and be appropriate to the type of work being undertaken. On navigable rivers the navigation authority should be notified before the boom is installed.

Case study 2.3
Oil spill – ground contamination (courtesy Kier)

About the site

Refurbishment of social housing near to a river, with temporary power provided to the small site office and storage compound by a power unit containing a generator and a fully bunded fuel tank.

Issue/incident

The unit was delivered to site direct from the manufacturer. It ran for several months before a leak was discovered in both the tank and the base of the bund. The leaking fuel soaked into the ground and eventually found its way into the river.

Site staff were able to deal with the fuel that found its way into the river effectively and quickly, but the clean-up of the contained soil and groundwater took several months.

Pollution prevention measure

☐ ground contamination was cleaned up using appropriate procedures

To stop this type of incident occurring again:

☐ introduce a generator log book that includes an inspection checklist, which should be completed daily

☐ make it a company requirement that refuelling can only be carried out by a named, competent operative.

Lessons learnt

☐ check that fuel storage tanks and bowers and all associated pipe work are in good order before filling

☐ ensure that fuel storage tanks and bowsers and all associated pipework are regularly checked for leaks

☐ monitor fuel usage – an abnormally high rate of consumption may indicate that the fuel storage tank is leaking

☐ report pollution incidents promptly to the environmental regulator and near misses to management.

2.5   Project assessment schemes

Within the construction industry there are a number of assessment schemes that are either directly designed to assess the environmental performance (and aspects of social and economical performance) of projects. These schemes reflect levels of industry good practice and in performance within the industry.

These schemes provide an ideal framework to demonstrate a project's environmental good practice intentions and reporting performance as well as ensuring further improvement. They do not replace the need for application of management controls, such as an EMS (see Section 2.1.7).

This section highlights some of the most commonly used schemes used, but by no means all. This guide supports these assessment schemes. Applying good practice from this guide, where appropriate, will further assist in demonstrating site performance.

Considerate Constructors Scheme (CCS) <www.ccscheme.org.uk>

Independent non-profit making scheme designed to improve the image of construction. Sites are assessed on a variety of criteria including health and safety, environmental management and community interaction. Assessment leads to site score and awards system. Although this is a voluntary scheme, it is increasingly required in contract conditions, including expected score to be achieved.

Civil Engineering Environmental Quality and Assessment Award Scheme (CEEQUAL) <www.ceequal.com>

CEEQUAL is the assessment and awards scheme for improving environmental and social performance in civil engineering and the public realm. It aims to deliver improved project specification, design and construction, and to demonstrate the commitment of the civil engineering industry to environmental quality and social performance.

The scheme rigorously assesses performance across 12 areas of environmental and social concern. It rewards project teams in which clients, designers and constructors go beyond the legal and environmental minima to achieve distinctive environmental and social standards. Awards are provided for demonstrable performance throughout the project.

Building Research Establishment Environmental Assessment Method (BREEAM) <www.breeam.org>

BREEAM is a series of environmental assessment schemes for buildings, developed and operated by Building Research Establishment (BRE). There are BREEAM assessment processes and tools for different sectors (eg education, retail, offices and prisons).

New assessment tools are developed to reflect needs in the building industry and the schemes are updated to reflect industry developments and expectations. Building design and construction processes are assessed and rated to provide an overall score, which is transferred into a building rating.

Leadership in Energy & Environmental Design (LEED) <www.usgbc.org>

LEED is an internationally recognised green building certification system, providing third party verification that a building or community was designed and built using strategies aimed at improving performance across all the key metrics: energy savings, water efficiency, CO_2 emissions reduction, improved indoor environmental quality, and stewardship of resources and sensitivity to their impacts.

Defence Related Environmental Assessment Methodology (DREAM) <www.dreamassess.com>

DREAM is an online environmental assessment tool for new building and refurbishment projects on defence estates.

Code for Sustainable Homes (CSH) <www.communities.gov.uk>

The Code measures the sustainability of a new home against nine categories of sustainable design, rating the "whole home" as a complete package. The Code uses a one to six star rating system to communicate the overall sustainability performance of a new home. By law, all new homes are required to be assessed under the CSH scheme and planning departments set minimum rating requirements dependent on their regional requirements.

Constructing Excellence Environmental Performance Indicators
<www.constructingexcellence.org.uk> and <www.kpizone.com>

Constructing Excellence produces a series of environmental indicators that aim to improve the industry. These can be applied to either benchmark a site's performance against industry standards, or to set targets for improvement.

3.1   Introduction

At every stage of the construction process there is the potential for effects on the environment to occur. This section contains a series of checklists to highlight some of the key issues that may be associated with a range of activities carried out on site during different stages of the construction process.

The checklists are not exhaustive, but are intended to include important issues that should be considered at each activity and stage. Reference is made to other sections of this guide to provide further advice.

It is intended that the checklists are reviewed to identify those activities and issues applicable to a particular site and then used to assess during site inspections whether or not they are being managed appropriately. Following this assessment the necessary changes to site practice can be carried out.

The checklists are divided into the following activities and sub-activities. In each case the sub-activities are listed in alphabetical order.

Pre-construction activities

- ☐   project planning
- ☐   site clearance
- ☐   site establishment
- ☐   site investigation
- ☐   temporary works.

Construction activities

- ☐   brick/blockwork
- ☐   concrete batching
- ☐   concrete pours and aftercare
- ☐   crushing, screening and reuse of materials
- ☐   demolition
- ☐   dredging earthworks
- ☐   excavation

☐   grouting

☐   landscaping/re-establishment

☐   piling

☐   refurbishment of buildings

☐   repairs to exposed structural elements (eg bridges, soffits, cladding)

☐   roadworks

☐   superstructure

☐   tunnelling.

Post-construction activities

☐   demobilisation

☐   permitting

☐   review activities (lessons learnt and good practice)

☐   site handover and commissioning.

Other important issues (applicable during all activities)

☐   use of hand tools

☐   use of plant and equipment

☐   use of oils and chemicals

☐   working near water

☐   working with groundwater.

3.2   Pre-construction activities

Project planning

Key issues	Refer to section
Identify environmental receptors on site	2.2
Identify environmental receptors around site	2.2
Identify environmental obligations for the contract (eg planning conditions, assessment schemes, environmental targets)	1.2
Identify applicable legislation	1.2
Define environmental responsibilities	2.1
Identify environmental risks	2.2
Develop environmental emergency response	2.4
Identify and plan site survey needs	2.2
Identify need to apply for permits and/or consents and licences (eg water abstraction, water discharge, waste) following completion of required surveys	2.2
Engage with regulators and local community	2.2
Develop environmental management plan (EMP)	2.1
Develop site waste management plan (SWMP)	2.2
Identify environmental training needs based on site requirements	2.2
Create environmental elements of site induction	2.2
Develop procurement strategy	2.2
Communicate site environmental requirements to the supply chain	2.2

Site clearance

Key issues	Refer to section
Follow established procedures if contaminated land is discovered	4.4.4
Location of protected species (wildlife and/or vegetation)	4.2.4
Measures to protect or process to relocate protected species (wildlife and/or vegetation)	4.2.5
Effect on local ecological habitats by altering ground conditions (eg disturbance of badger setts)	4.2.5
Removal and reinstatement of vegetation (habitat translocation)	4.2.7
Archaeological finds (including human remains)	4.3.6, 4.3.7
Noise, dust and vibration created during operations (eg movement of materials around site)	4.1.4, 4.6.3
Pollution of site water supply or nearby watercourses	4.9.9, 4.6.7
Reuse of materials where possible (eg brickwork for hardcore)	4.8.5, 4.5.4
Waste disposal in accordance with regulations (eg waste carrier's licence)	4.8.10, 4.8.11

Site establishment

Key issues	Refer to section
Determine most appropriate location for the placement of site offices and facilities	2.2
Define storage areas for materials fuels and oils	2.2
Define storage area for materials to be reused on site	2.2
Define waste facilities and facilities on site	2.2
Identify and protect drainage	2.2, 4.9.9
Identify and protect surface and groundwater	2.2, 4.9.3
Identify all underground services before work starts	2.2
Determine most appropriate location of vehicle wash off facilities	2.2
Create concrete wash off areas	2.2
Establish site hoarding/site fencing	2.2

Site investigation

Key issues	Refer to section
Identify the scope of ecology surveys	4.2.4
Identify contaminated land (desktop and intrusive investigations)	4.4.3
Identify the scope of archaeological investigation	4.3.2

Temporary works

Key issues	Refer to section
Ensure that required permissions have been sought before any works begin. For example Section 61 consent from the local authority	4.6.4
Take care when carrying out temporary works near watercourses	4.9.9
On-site fabrication of steelwork may be noisy and annoy neighbours	2.4.3, 4.6.3
Reuse materials on site or off site	4.8.5

3.3 Construction activities

Brick/blockwork

Key issues	Refer to section
Avoid unnecessary wastage of materials by: ☐ not over-ordering materials ☐ storing in packaging to protect them ☐ storing away from vehicle movements ☐ preventing ready-mixed mortar from drying out ☐ avoiding cutting and chasing	4.5.2, 4.5.4
Reuse of excess bricks or blocks, either on or off site. If damaged use them as hardcore on site access roads	4.5.4
Segregate and recycle of packaging wastes	4.8.9
Reduce dust nuisance from cutting and chasing	4.1.4

Concrete batching

Key issues	Refer to section
Minimise visual, noise and dust disturbance to neighbours. Plant is likely to require authorisation under the Environmental Protection Act 1990	2.3.1, 4.1.4, 4.6.3
Minimise nuisance to neighbours from noise of motors and conveyors	4.6.3
Minimise wastage and contamination of aggregates during storage	4.5.4, 4.5.5
Store and dispose of additives to prevent spillage and contamination	4.5.5
Surface drainage from the area around the batching plant may be polluted, so permit/licence/consents' required to store and dispose	4.9.3, 4.9.6
Accurate prediction of volume required to avoid over production and wastage	4.9.7
Potential of highly alkaline washout from mixing plant or cleaning of ready-mix concrete lorries contaminating watercourses	4.9.6
Release of concrete from concreting operations that are near or in watercourses (floating batchers)	4.9.9
Recycle returned concrete to reduce washout volumes and produce viable aggregate	4.5.4
Potential of alkaline cement dust released from silos during filling to harm ecology and annoy neighbours	4.1.2, 4.1.4
When cleaning silos, reverse jet filters will minimise dust emissions by capturing and reusing cement dust	4.1.4
Prevent of overfilling and spillage from pipelines and pumps because of poor maintenance	2.4
Maintain plant well to prevent noise and emissions	4.1.4, 4.6.3

Concrete pours and aftercare

Key issues	Refer to section
Control the storage, handling and disposal of shutter oils	4.5.5
Consider using suction opposed to blowing dust and debris out of formwork, so not to annoy neighbours	4.1.4
Ensure concrete batching plant has a dust suppression system installed and a high level alarm to prevent overfilling	4.1.4
Carry out pre-use checks on ready mix concrete wagons to check for defects, in particular hydraulic hoses, especially when works are being carried out in or near watercourses	4.9.9
Consider the wastes that will be generated and plan their handling and disposal. For example concrete curing compounds (spray applications), blackjack waterproofing (silane), PVC sheeting, frost protection materials	4.8.9
A concrete pour may displace wastewaters from the hole. These may be contaminated with sediment and cleaning materials from the side of the structure. Dispose of them appropriately	4.9.6
In or near a watercourse, control the placing of any wet concrete to minimise the risk of cement leaking into the watercourse. Shutter failure in such locations can cause major pollution in the watercourse	4.9.9
The washout from a concrete mixing plant, or and from the cleaning of ready-mix concrete lorries, is contaminated with cement and so is highly alkaline. Do not allow it to enter any watercourse or groundwaters. Alternatively consider returning the wagon to the batching plant to wash out the container, ie only wash out the chute on site to minimise wash waters on site	4.9.9
To dispose of washout water obtain consent and dispose of it to the foul sewer via a settling tank	4.9.6
Large areas of concrete can create dust when dry, so sweep regularly	4.1.4

Crushing, screening and reuse of materials

Key issues	Refer to section
Under the Environmental Protection Act 1990 and under Waste and Contaminated Land (NI) Order authorisation will be needed to operate a crusher and screener on site. An exemption for the reuse of crushed material maybe required, check with regulator	2.3.1
Ensure to work within the requirements of the consent in terms of emissions, working hours and monitoring regime	2.3.1, 4.1.4
When operating a crusher ensure it is sited away from sensitive receptors	4.6.3
Ensure the discharge from crushers and screens onto conveyors is enclosed as far as practicable to minimise the effects of noise and dust	4.6.3, 4.1.4
Stockpiled material should be suitably covered to prevent dust arising	4.1.4, 4.5.5
Ensure road transport of screened/crushed material is sheeted/in covered wagons	4.1.4, 4.7.1
Ensure effective use of crushed and screened materials on site	4.5.4

Demolition

Key issues	Refer to section
Locate and mark all underground pipes, tanks and services. Also label all tanks with their content and capacity. Check for any visible signs of leaking tanks or pipes, and any signs of contaminated ground or groundwater	4.9.3, 4.4.3
Review the disposal options for the materials that will be generated. Reclaim and reuse materials where possible. Identify markets for materials. Segregate materials as they are generated. Label waste clearly and store in a designated area. Dispose of any materials in accordance with the duty of care	4.8.9, 4.5.4
If materials such as concrete or masonry are to be crushed on site, ensure that any necessary licences/permit is obtained from the local environmental health officer in England, Wales and Northern Ireland or SEPA in Scotland	2.1.2, 2.2
Before removing or perforating tanks, check that all of their contents and residues have been emptied for safe disposal by a competent operator. Pipes may contain significant quantities of oil or chemicals, and should be capped, or valves closed, to prevent spillage. Ensure that suitable spill response materials and emergency instructions are available on site and that staff have been adequately trained	2.4, 4.8.10
All asbestos should be dealt with by a registered contractor. Ensure the locations of materials containing asbestos are identified through a formal site survey before starting work	4.8.10
Noise and vibration may annoy neighbours. Consider screening the works	2.3.1, 4.6.3
Dust from the demolition process may annoy neighbours and damage ecology near the site. Damp down structures during demolition. Ensure that any runoff from the site is prevented from entering watercourses or soakaways	4.1.4, 4.9.9
If elephant chutes are being used, ensure that each section is securely fixed, that the skip or lorry at the discharge end is covered, and that materials are dampened before being sent down the chute	4.1.4
Prevent dust escaping from materials in lorries leaving the site. If it is not possible to cover lorries because there are pieces of protruding material, spray them with water just before they leave	4.1.4

Dredging

Key issues	Refer to section
Dredgings may be contaminated with substances such as oils and heavy metals; sample and test the sediments to provide vital information for considering disposal options	4.8.10
Aim to reuse the dredgings (for example, to improve agricultural land) rather than disposing of them to landfill	4.5.4
Ensure pre-consultation with the regulator and interested parties, eg boat clubs and riparian owners, before dredging works start	2.3
Plan the disposal of dredgings before starting works, to allow time for obtaining any permissions required under appropriate waste management licensing/permitting regulations	2.1.2, 4.8.8
Disposing of dredgings at sea requires a licence. It can take up to three months to obtain a licence for a new site from Defra or Marine Scotland	
Dredging materials contaminated with heavy metals or oils may lead to the production of materials classified as hazardous waste, and as such appropriate disposal will be required	4.8.10
If landfilling the dredgings, obtain an exemption from landfill tax for dredgings arising from maintenance of navigable inland waterways	4.8.10
Obtain a discharge consent for returning effluent from dewatering dredgings to controlled waters	4.9.6
The dewatering sediments may cause an odour problem	4.1.5
Dredging may affect the aquatic ecology, so should be undertaken outside the fish spawning season. Use an appropriate dredging technique, eg dredge mats and silt curtains, to minimise the disturbance of sediment resulting in silting of the watercourse and potential mobilisation of contaminants	4.9.3
Disturbance of organic silts and dying weed may give rise to deoxygenation. Monitor and aerate if necessary. Undertake outside fish spawning season	4.9.3
Working with compacted sediments may generate high levels of noise. Also, mechanical dewatering and compaction may lead to vibration	4.6.3

Earthworks

Key issues	Refer to section
Minimise the surplus materials arising from earthworks by considering methods of improving the spoil (eg in situ stabilisation)	4.5.4
Dispose of surplus materials arising from earthworks in accordance with appropriate duty of care regulations. Testing of the spoil may be required to provide information for considering disposal options. Aim to reuse spoil, eg for land profiling and raising, rather than disposing of it to landfill. Be aware that reuse needs to be in accordance with planning permission, eg land profiling/raising and may need an exemption from a permit	4.8.6, 4.8.10
Be aware of unexpected contamination revealed during earthworks. Halt works immediately, clear the site and seek expert advice	4.4.4
Be aware of unexpected archaeological finds. Materials to look out for during excavations include burned or blackened material, brick or tile fragments, coins, pottery or bone fragments, skeletons, timber joints or post holes, brick or stone foundations, infilled ditches	4.3.3
Be aware of unexpected ecological finds, for example the presence of newts. Should any species be found stop work immediately and seek expert advice	4.2.4
Keep water away from unsurfaced areas using measures such as cut-off drains. Control and dispose of silty water in a controlled manner, all discharges other than clean rainwater, eg storm drainage, excavation dewatering wastewater, may require a consent. Adequate treatment (eg settlement) should be provided before discharge	4.9.3, 4.9.6
Earthmoving plant and vehicles used to transport materials from and around the site may cause impacts from emissions, mud and noise. Construct appropriate haul roads. Maintain plant and vehicles. Use road sweepers, manual sweeping, scraping and jet washing to minimise mud/debris on roads	4.1.4, 4.6.3, 4.7.2

Excavation

Key issues	Refer to section
Prevent water entering excavations. When water does enter excavations, take measures to avoid it becoming contaminated. Dispose of it properly	4.9.4, 4.9.6
Be aware of unexpected archaeological finds. Materials to look out for during excavations include: burned or blackened material, brick or tile fragments, coins, pottery or bone fragments, skeletons, timber joints or post holes, brick or stone foundations, infilled ditches. If any unexpected finds are encountered stop work immediately and seek expert advice	4.3.3
If excavation reveals contamination, halt digging immediately. Clear the site immediately and where appropriate, try as far as possible to identify the extent and cause of contamination (eg spillage on site, rupture of subterranean pipeline) and attempt to contain contaminants. Seek expert advice	2.4, 4.4.4
If asbestos is uncovered unexpectedly during digging operations, halt digging operations at once and refill the excavation. Exposure of asbestos to the open air can result in widespread contamination far from the site as the particles are easily airborne. Remove personnel immediately and secure the area. Contact site management immediately	4.8.10
Excavation plant and vehicles used to transport materials from and around the site may cause adverse effects such as from emissions, mud and noise. Poorly maintained plant and vehicles cause more environmental effects than well-maintained plant	2.2.5, 4.1.4, 4.6.3, 4.7.2
Use a wheel wash to minimise dirt on public highway	4.9.3
Spoil arising from excavation can be recycled if not contaminated. Crush any rock arising and use on or off site. Store topsoil for reuse in piles less than two metres high to prevent damage to the soil structure. Use excavated materials to form noise bunds and for landscaping – check whether planning permission/exemption is required	4.5.5, 4.6.3

Grouting

Key issues	Refer to section
Blowback from blockages or overfilling from pressure grouting with dry materials, eg cement, can cause significant dust problems. Working within an enclosure may be necessary in particularly sensitive areas	4.1.4
Grouting in or near contaminated ground may displace polluted water in the excavation. Prevent the uncontrolled release of this water	4.9.3, 4.9.6
Prevent the uncontrolled discharge of cements and bentonite slurries. Use a settlement tank to remove sediments and obtain a discharge consent before releasing the effluent	4.9.5, 4.9.6
Grout waste can be more successfully separated by the addition of a chemical flocculant, or by hydroclone separation or mechanical dewatering. This allows easier disposal of the constituents	4.9.5
Deal with any slurry waste (water mixed with silt) appropriately	4.9.3

Landscaping/re-establishment

Key issues	Refer to section
Refer to the biodiversity action plan (BAP). It is beneficial to select a range of native species to maintain local biodiversity	4.2.4
Consider the use and location when selecting species, eg when landscaping inclines, select appropriate species mix for gradient and to help prevent soil erosion	4.2.8
Consider the visual impacts and maintenance requirements when designing the landscaping. This should take consideration of the local stakeholders and intended users	2.2
Consider early landscaping to offer some noise, dust and visual screening	4.1.4, 4.6.3
Note that hard landscaping may increase flood risk. Ensure appropriate drainage is provided to accommodate runoff	4.9.3
Segregate and reuse excavated materials, topsoil and subsoil for use during landscaping	4.5.5

Piling

Key issues	Refer to section
If recycled aggregates are used as the piling mat an environmental permit/exemption would be needed for the reuse of this recycled material; if it has not been produced in conformance to the WRAP quality protocol	4.5.2
Maintain plant regularly to optimise fuel efficiency	2.4
Minimise the risk of spillage in using oils and chemicals	2.4
Noise and vibration may annoy neighbours. The noise levels created by piling vary with the method used. Some methods will not be allowed in urban areas, or other sensitive locations where the site has immediate residential neighbours – so use the right plant	4.6.3
Manage bentonite appropriately to prevent its release to the environment. Recycle if possible or dispose of it properly	4.5.4, 4.9.3
Manage wastes arising from the piling operations. Wastes from bored piling may be a particular problem as it is often wet. Dispose of this waste in a controlled manner	4.8.10
Piling close to watercourses forms a potential pollution risk	4.9.9, 4.9.3
Contaminated ground may be encountered, which could introduce a pathway that contaminants, mobilised by groundwater, may escape through. It is important to develop a contingency plan for dealing with it. If it is encountered, halt works, clear the site and seek expert advice	4.4.2
Contaminated spoil should be stored separately from other materials and be disposed of according to appropriate hazardous (special) waste regulations	4.8.10

Refurbishment of buildings

Key issues	Refer to section
Explore the opportunities for reusing and recycling materials in the refurbishment. These materials may have arisen as waste on site or may originate off site	4.5.4
There is a risk of exposing asbestos during the works, for example, by drilling into walls and ceilings. Ask the building owner and/or manager for detailed information on the location of asbestos in the building. Seek advice on what action to take if asbestos is found	4.8.10
Any wastes arising from the works should be handled appropriately and disposed of in accordance with legislation	4.8.10
Noise and vibration from works may annoy the building's inhabitants	4.6.3, 4.6.7
Use debris netting when carrying out external refurbishment eg cladding, to reduce dust and protect against falling objects	4.1.4

Repairs to exposed structural elements (eg bridge soffits, cladding)

Key issues	Refer to section
Prevent debris from works falling onto the ground or water below. This should be incorporated into the working methods. It is especially important for works over public areas or near watercourses and sensitive ecological sites	4.9.9
Store hazardous materials carefully to minimise the risk of spillage	2.2.4, 4.5.5
Noise from the works may annoy neighbours	2.3.1, 4.6.3
Carrying out repairs over a watercourse has potential to pollute it	4.9.9

Roadworks

Key issues	Refer to section
Minimise the risk of spillage in using oils, bitumens and chemicals	2.4
Noise and vibration may annoy neighbours. Night time working may cause additional annoyance. Ensure appropriate dust management techniques are used when removing upper layers of road surface and planing	2.3.1, 4.6.3, 4.6.7
Traffic entering and leaving the site may disrupt normal traffic flow. Emissions from traffic may annoy neighbours	4.1.5, 4.7.2
Much of the waste material arising from roadworks can be recycled	4.5.4
Do not discharge gully pot residues to ground or surface waters. Alternative disposal options include discharging to the foul sewer (with the consent of the local sewerage provider) after solids settlement, or at a suitably licensed waste disposal site	4.9.6

Superstructure

Key issues	Refer to section
Installation of large structures may require night time working or road closures, ensure appropriate consents are obtained and notifications are made	4.6.4
Consideration should be given to off-site pre-fabrication to minimise on site impacts	4.5.2

Tunnelling

Key issues	Refer to section
Impacts on groundwater, which could have subsequent impacts on ecological habitats	4.2.4
May require an abstraction license/permit and/or discharge consent/permit depending on disposal. Disposal of excess water should be done in a controlled manner	4.9.6
Disposal of spoil and slurry arising from tunnelling works and traffic associated with long distance transport	4.7.2
Buildings sensitive to ground-borne vibration in the locality of planned ground level tunnels	4.6.7
24-hour working causing annoyance to neighbours near the tunnel portal	2.3.1, 4.6.3
Encountering contaminated ground or groundwater during tunnelling. Follow the steps below if encountered: ● stop work immediately ● report the discovery to the site manager who should seek expert advice ● seal off the area to contain spread of contaminants ● clear site to ensure there is nothing that could cause fire or explosion ● contact the regulator or local authority once it is confirmed that contamination is found ● ensure that the suspected contamination is tested and characterised and agree changes to the existing remedial plan ● follow good practice guidance to remediate the land	4.4.4
Discovery of archaeological finds (including old cemeteries)	4.3.3
Subsidence caused in listed building in locality of tunnel portal	4.3.8

3.4   Post construction activities

Demobilisation

Key issues	Refer to section
Ensure boreholes have been decommissioned effectively to avoid leaving pathways for pollutants	4.4.2
Demobilisation will give rise to a number of waste streams especially hazardous waste through closure of COSHH stores. Ensure appropriate disposal	4.8.10
Ensure close-out of redundant, or handover of ongoing permits and consents, eg drainage consents, abstraction licence and IPC permit	2.2
Ensure necessary contracts are in place to fulfil any ongoing monitoring requirements, eg ecological	2.2, 4.2.4

Permitting

Key issues	Refer to section
Surrender/transfer abstraction licences (soon to be environmental permits (EPs)), ie abstraction licence obtained for an on-site borehole, water from which was used for dust suppression	2.2, 4.9.6
Transfer discharge consents (EPs) for elements of the permanent works as required, ie discharge consent (EP) for newly constructed wheel wash facility	2.2, 4.9.6
Surrender EP for use of waste material on-site	2.2, 4.8.8

Review activities (lessons learnt and good practice)

Key issues	Refer to section
Complete final assessment of site waste management plan (SWMP), including assessment of cost savings and identification of good practice	4.8.9
Write up case studies/results of trials undertaken or new technologies used and promote within company/to industry	2.2

Site handover and commissioning

Key issues	Refer to section
Provide all necessary documentation, including handover manuals etc, are completed and issued	2.2
Ensure calibration of monitoring equipment before handover	2.2
Ensure maintenance requirements for critical equipment/plant are detailed and handed over	2.2
Ensure handover of any ongoing permits, licences and consents (PLCs)	2.2
If required provide training in use of IT systems/equipment/plant etc for operating team	2.2

3.5 Other important issues (applicable during all activities)

Use of handheld tools

Key issues	Refer to section
Develop a refuelling protocol for the site and follow it	4.5.6
Maintain plant regularly to optimise fuel efficiency and prevent pollution incidents	
Prevent water pollution and ground contamination. Use drip trays under stationary plant to contain oil leaks	2.4
Ensure that only trained personnel use plant and that they use it for its intended purpose	
Remember that water containing oils or other chemical contamination cannot be discharged to watercourses or on to the ground	4.9.6
Secure plant from vandals, as they could cause pollution incidents	2.3.3
Noise and vibration from plant (eg generators and poker vibrators) may annoy neighbours and disturb ecology. Where possible, use quiet plant	4.6.3, 4.6.7

Use of plant and equipment

Key issues	Refer to section
Designate an area within the site compound for routine plant maintenance. Ensure that the plant maintenance area in on hardstanding and is remote from surface water drains	2.2
Surface water runoff from plant maintenance may contain pollutants, eg oils. Prevent their release to controlled waters	4.9.3
Ensure that appropriately trained personnel carry out repairs to plant	
Develop a protocol for disposing of wastes from maintenance	4.8.10
Dispose of old filters carefully as they contain substantial quantities of oil; all engine oils/waste oils (except edible oils) are hazardous/special waste.	4.8.10
Encourage the use of biodegradable oil substitutes over non-biodegradable where appropriate	4.5.2
Recycle used oils	4.5.4
Tyres cannot be sent to landfill, therefore find an appropriate route for recycling them	4.5.4
Prepare for spillages. Display the site's emergency response procedure at the plant maintenance area. Ensure a spillage kit is kept there and that all personnel know how to use it. Carry a spill kit in all repair vehicles	2.4
Check replacement periods for hydraulic pipework and carry out regular checks. Use biodegradable oil for hydraulics where appropriate. Blowouts regularly cause pollution incidents	2.4

Use of oils and chemicals

Key issues	Refer to section
Control of Substances Hazardous to Health (COSHH) assessments need to be held on site for any potentially hazardous materials. These provide advice on the type of storage needed for the chemicals, ie bunded areas, storage of flammable products in locked cupboards	4.5.5
Well managed and maintained storage of hazardous materials reduces waste and the risk of spillages, which could result in possible ground or groundwater contamination. Store all potentially polluting substances away from surface and foul water drains, watercourses and sensitive areas	4.5.5
Oil storage must be in accordance with Control of Pollution (Oil Storage) (England) Regulations 2001 or The Water Environment (Oil Storage) (Scotland) Regulations 2006. These regulations do not apply in Northern Ireland and Wales, but consideration should be taken to meet the requirements as they are designed to prevent contamination of the water environment, which would be an offence under other legislation	4.5.5
Transfer chemicals between containers only within a suitably bunded area. Spillages outside this area could result in ground or water contamination	4.9.3
When using fuel, follow the refuelling protocol to minimise the risk of spillage	4.5.6
Minimise accidental spillages and have emergency procedures in place in case of a spill. Ensure there is a spill kit available and personnel are trained to use it	2.4
Any disposal of product or empty product containers should be in accordance with waste management legislation and the related COSHH datasheet	4.5.5
Provide security measures for the site and storage areas to prevent vandalism and theft. Storage system valves, taps, hatches or lids and delivery hoses should be fitted with locks and locked when not in use. Where possible materials should be stored in secure containers or buildings	2.2, 4.5.5

Working near water

Key issues	Refer to section
Check that permission has been obtained for any temporary works	4.9.9
Special consideration needs to be taken when working on pontoons and barges	4.9.9
Supervise closely all plant refuelling. Fill portable fuel tanks and spare fuel containers away from the water's edge and never overfill	4.5.6
Keep adequate supplies of booms and oil absorbent material available at all times for emergency use in case of a spillage. Dispose of any used absorbents in accordance with duty of care	2.4, 4.8.6
Prevent pollution from plant used near a watercourse. Maintain plant regularly. Use drip trays	4.9.9
Ensure that the runoff from haul roads near or over watercourses cannot enter the watercourse	4.9.9
Erect temporary haul road bridges to prevent pollution and damage to stream beds	4.9.3
Where watercourse embankments are stripped of vegetation, stabilise them to prevent erosion. This may be done by seeding them using clover or fast growing grasses and covering with biodegradable sheeting	
Prevent dust or litter blowing into watercourses	4.1.4, 4.9.9
Be aware of potential direct or indirect disturbance to the bankside and in-stream ecology	4.2.4
Ensure that works are secured from vandals	2.3.3

Working with groundwater

Key issues	Refer to section
Notify the environmental regulator where extensive dewatering is to occur so they may issue the relevant licence/permit	4.9.6
Any groundwater abstracted from site needs to be disposed of. Generally the best environmental option is to return it to groundwater. Seek advice from the environmental regulator before adopting this solution as a discharge consent may be required	4.9.6
There is a risk of mobilising ground contamination when working with groundwater and a potential risk of ground instability. If any contamination is suspected, seek specialist advice before proceeding	4.4.2, 4.4.4
Consider monitoring for petrol/oil or diesel compounds that will float on the groundwater surface and move with the flow of water	4.9.9
Works affecting groundwater may have an effect on nearby ecology. Seek specialist ecological advice before any works are carried out	4.2.4
Dewatering may cause a change in groundwater levels and affect river/stream flows. A solution is to monitor water levels in sensitive areas and recharge with the extracted groundwater of the correct quality and temperature	4.9.6
Minimise the risk of spillage when using oils and chemicals	2.4

4.1   Dust, emissions and odours

4.1.1   Introduction

Dust is considered to be any airborne particulate matter up to 75μm in diameter. In addition to causing a nuisance to neighbouring properties and vehicles, dust may lead to several health issues including eye, nose and throat irritation as well as exposure to respirable dust exacerbating asthma. Also, dust may cause adverse ecological impacts to both aquatic and non aquatic plants and animals.

Emissions from plant and generators may cause air pollution and odours. These smaller particles may be inhaled leading to respiratory problems and long-term cardiovascular health issues. Odours associated with waste organic material, sewage or even cooking also can cause nuisance.

Where the local authority considers that a statutory nuisance is occurring then an abatement notice must be served. This may have cost, programme and reputational implications for the project team. Legal claims may arise for expenses, for example associated with car washing and window cleaning or damage to crops in rural areas.

Common sources of dust, emissions and odours are:

☐   unpaved haul roads

☐   mud on public roads

☐   tipping

☐   uncovered vehicle movements

☐   material stockpiles

☐   cutting, grinding and drilling operations

☐   shot-blasting

☐   earthworks.

4.1.2   Why is the management of dust, emissions and odours important?

Dust, emissions and odours arising from a site can cause health risks to site personnel and neighbours, air pollution, and annoyance to local residents.

Legal action, under either criminal or common law is possible and could result in delays, costs and damage to reputation.

Dust particle sizes can vary considerably, depending on their origin, and the smallest particles can be inhaled. Some dust, such as limestone, is chemically active and inert dusts such as silica are associated with lung disease. Emissions from plant and generators can pollute the atmosphere and create unpleasant odours.

Neighbours

Annoyance is caused when residents have to re-clean washing and when they have to wash cars, curtains and windows. Wind-blown dust can be unsightly over long distances in scenic areas. In exceptional circumstances dust can affect health, for example by causing eye irritation. Asthma can be exacerbated by exposure to respirable dust.

 The managing director of Cosy Developments was fined more than £18 000 after the company started green vegetation bonfires at a residential development in breach of a previously issued abatement notice.

Dust impacts on crops and ecology

Claims are particularly common on rural road projects. Even very low concentrations of dust can affect plant and fruit growth. Plant growth is especially susceptible to dusts that are highly alkaline, for example cement dust. Claims for damage to crops in excess of half a mile from the site have been made because dust can be blown for long distances. Also with the growth of "organic" farming, there have been claims resulting from contamination by dust-borne pesticides and fertilisers. Dust blowing onto watercourses can damage the ecology. Ash trees may drop their leaves up to eight weeks early following exposure to high levels of dust.

Impact on project programme and budget

Some contracts may specify that no work occurs at times of high wind in a certain direction. Working to comply with strict dust levels can impose cost and/or programme constraints. If a statutory nuisance is occurring an abatement notice must be served by the local authority.

4.1.3   Legal requirements

Under the Environmental Protection Act (EPA) 1990, local authorities are required to inspect their areas and investigate any complaints made relating to dust, emissions and odour nuisance. Statutory nuisances can result in abatement notices being served when complaints have been received.

To avoid causing complaints, the site should adopt good working practices:

☐   identify sensitive receptors and any activities likely to give rise to dust, odours or emissions affecting residential/surrounding land uses, schools, wildlife, statutory designations and watercourses

☐   in liaison with the local authority develop a dust control plan and adopt control measures to mitigate any negative effects (eg site speed limits, use of water bowsers, sheeting of vehicles and skips)

☐   undertake daily monitoring and keep a record of dust management activities and any complaints received

☐   respond to monitoring results and any complaints received and notify the local authority of any actions taken.

Note: The monitoring regime should link into the management plan to trigger preventative measures and actions when monitoring results indicate elevated dust levels. Also, the regime should note weather conditions, construction activities, their location and duration on site. The dust control plan should employ best practicable means (BPM).

4.1.4   How to avoid problems

Dust suppression

It is important to develop a strategy to stop dust being generated. Careful planning and design of construction operations can reduce dust for example:

☐   use of appropriate surfaces (ie tarmac) and speed limits on haul routes

☐   use of rumble strips

☐   damping down

☐   wheel washing

☐   road sweeping

☐   manual sweeping

□   jet washing

□   scraping to remove excess build ups of materials on site

□   haul vehicle covers

□   locating stockpiles and batching plant in sheltered areas

□   rolling and seeding stockpiles

□   chemical binders applied to stockpiles or exposed ground

□   water suppression on cutting, grinding and drilling

□   enclosing areas where shot-blasting is undertaken.

Figure 4.1
Dust suppression (courtesy Parsons Brinckerhoff)

Damp down using water

Fine spraying of water (eg using a bowser as shown in Figure 4.1) is the most effective way to suppress dust. Repeat spray regularly, especially during warm and sunny weather when water will evaporate quickly. However, ensure that the application does not create excessive mud that can runoff into watercourses.

Consider spraying:

□   unpaved work areas subject to traffic or wind

□   structures and buildings during demolition

□   sand, spoil and aggregate stockpiles

□   during the loading and unloading of dust generating materials.

If abstracting water for spraying from a watercourse or fire hydrant, ensure to have obtained the appropriate consent (see Section 4.9.6).

Damp down using water with chemical additives or binders

Damping down, using water in dry weather only offers a temporary solution. For a longer lasting solution it may be appropriate to mix additives and chemical binders to the water. Spraying with water and chemical additives is more effective than using water alone because this will reduce the number of passes per day and the volume of water needed.

There are several additives on the market and the cost of the additives has to be considered against savings in water supply, bowser use, downtime and ecological risk. Take care to avoid over application that may cause pollution. Seek advice from the environmental regulator before using additives, especially if close to a watercourse or abstraction point.

Dust screening

If dust-generating activities cannot be avoided, it may help to erect screens to act as windbreaks or dust screens. These can take the form of permeable or semi-permeable fences, but they can be expensive if designed to resist high winds. Trees or shrubs planted early, as part of site landscaping, can provide some screening as can the retention of existing vegetation (or buildings to be demolished). Also, in building demolition, retention of external walls while internal demolition and deconstruction is being undertaken will offer dust screening.

Dust prediction and monitoring

There are several methods for monitoring dust on site, these include:

1   Exposing microscope slides or sticky pads for a given period to determine dust direction and deposition rate over the exposed period.

2   Using high volume samplers to draw air through a filter to measure the volume of dust in the air at the time.

3   Using a dry Frisbee dust deposit gauge (shown in Figure 4.2) to collect large and small dust particles over one month intervals. The contents are then sent for analysis to determine deposition rates.

Figure 4.2
Dust monitoring
(courtesy Balfour Beatty)

For all methods used samples need to be obtained before work starts to determine background levels for comparison against those taken during construction.

None of these methods provide definitive evidence of the effects of dust. If they are to be used to demonstrate commitment to good practice, then the cost needs to be accounted for in the long-term budget. It may be difficult to justify discontinuing monitoring once it has started. However, monitoring data may be useful evidence in defence of a nuisance claim.

For a dust monitoring programme to give more definitive evidence of the effects of construction it should include both upwind and downwind monitoring of the site and cover a baseline period before construction started. Monitoring ensures any potentially sensitive receptors are covered, eg schools. The baseline period should ideally cover the same seasons as the construction period. Often this level of monitoring is not recommended unless required by the contract or if the impact of dust is expected to be significant.

As general good practice, carry out regular visual checks of dust across the site and keep a log of the results. Monitor complaints from members of the public and rectify substantiated complaints. On large construction sites agree air quality action levels with the local authority and adopt a mitigation strategy if these levels are breached.

Cement manufacturer Cemex UK Cement Limited was fined £20 000 and ordered to pay £13 469 in costs after accepting responsibility for breaking their permit conditions under the Pollution Prevention and Control Regulations 2000 by causing coal dust to be released over homes and cars in Rugby. The nuisance was caused by the overfilling of one of the coal storage silos as a result of a failure to maintain an alarm mechanism in place to prevent such overflows.

4.1.5   Emissions and odours

Processes involving the use of fuels and the heating and drying of materials commonly emit fumes, odours or smoke. It is important to prevent emissions and odours as far as possible (refer to checklist in Section 4.1.6).

Any works that risk creating odours should be planned appropriately so as to minimise any effect.

Any processes that emit fumes, odours or smoke should comply with the manufacturer and if appropriate regulatory limits to prevent nuisance.

All plant should comply with EU emission limits for their vehicle class as a minimum and should be regularly maintained. A programme of maintenance checks should be developed for plant on site and adhered to.

Dark smoke from plant and fires is a statutory nuisance. The local authority may serve notices to stop those activities generating the smoke.

If plant or machinery emits excessive (ie amounting to nuisance) levels of exhaust emissions, local authorities have the power to prescribe limits on those emissions, the breaching of which may be an offence. Old plant, or plant carrying out an operation it is not designed for, can be likely to fall foul of the prescribed limit.

Consider fitting exhaust filtration systems to vehicles. Ensure any plant and equipment emitting black smoke is taken out of service immediately and the defect rectified. As far as possible locate plant away from sensitive receptors, ie neighbours and local ecology. Where possible use mains or battery powered equipment over diesel powered.

Mid UK Recycling Ltd was ordered to pay approximately £5000 in fines and costs for breaching a condition of their permit by allowing bad smells to escape from the site in contravention of the Environmental Permitting Regulations 2007. The smell, which upset local residents, was caused by a combination of lack of active management at the site, waste acceptance procedures not being followed, a failure to incorporate larger woody materials into very wet grass-based waste and having too much waste on site.

4.1.6   Good practice checklists

 Good housekeeping

Haul routes

Select suitable haul routes away from sensitive receptors if possible. Reduce the length and width of haul roads (while still allowing two way traffic) to minimise the surface area that dust may be produced from	
Temporary surface heavily used areas, or use geotextiles (eg around batching plant or haul routes). Sweep these regularly	
Carry out regular road sweeping, manual sweeping, scraping and jet washing to remove excess build-up of materials on site and public roads	
Limit vehicle speeds – the slower the vehicle the less the dust generation	
Damp down	

Demolition

Use enclosed chutes for dropping demolition materials that have the potential to cause dust. Regularly dampen the chutes	
Obtain consent from the regulator for the use of mobile plant for crushing materials such as bricks, tiles and concrete	
Use debris netting during demolition to reduce dust emissions	
Locate crushing plant away from sensitive receptors	

Plant and vehicles

Clean the wheels of vehicles leaving the site so that mud is not spread onto the highways	

Ensure that exhaust fumes are directed upwards and not directly at the ground	
Retractable sheeted covers on vehicles should be used to enclose dust	
Ensure all plant and vehicles are in good working order with an up-to-date maintenance log	
Vehicles should keep to site speed limits to reduce the risk of dust clouds	
Ensure vehicles carrying dusty loads are securely covered before leaving site	
As far as possible locate plant away from sensitive receptors	
Materials handling and storage	
Locate stockpiles out of the wind (or provide wind breaks) to minimise the potential for dust generation	
Keep the stockpiles to the minimum practicable height and use gentle slopes	
Re-vegetate long-term stockpiles and consider use of chemical dust suppressant additives for short term control	
Minimise the storage time of materials on site	
Store materials away from the site boundary, main site access roads and downwind of sensitive receptors	
Ensure all waste skips are enclosed or covered by tarpaulin	
Minimise the height of fall of materials	
Damp down earthworks during dry weather	
Concrete batching	
Mix large quantities of concrete or bentonite slurries in enclosed areas to avoid generating dust	
Cutting/grinding/grouting/packing	
Minimise cutting and grinding on site where possible	
On cutters and saws, use equipment and techniques such as dust extractors to minimise dust. Consider a wet cutting saw or use vacuum extraction or block splitters	
Spray water during cutting of paving slabs to minimise dust	

Preventing emissions and odours

Vehicles and plant

Ensure vehicles and plant used on site are well maintained and regularly serviced. Ensure that all vehicles used by contractors comply with MOT emissions standards at all times	
Control deliveries to site to minimise queuing	
Make sure that engines are switched off when they are not in use	
Keep refuelling areas away from the public	

Waste storage

To avoid odours use covered containers for organic waste (eg food, weeds and other vegetation) and remove waste frequently	

Chemicals on site

To avoid odours: ☐ take account of the wind conditions when arranging activities that are likely to emit aerosols, fumes, odours and smoke ☐ position site toilets away from residential areas	

4.1.7   Further guidance

DEFRA, SCOTTISH EXECUTIVE and WELSH ASSEMBLY GOVERNMENT (2004) Process Guidance Note 3/16 (04) *Secretary of State's Guidance for mobile crushing and screening* *

ENVIRONMENT AGENCY, SEPA and NIEA (2010) Pollution Prevention Guidelines (PPG) 6 *Working at construction and demolition sites* *

GREATER LONDON AUTHORITY (2006) *The control of dust and emissions from construction and demolition – best practice guidance*, Greater London Authority, London *

OFFICE OF THE DEPUTY PRIME MINISTER (2005) Minerals Policy Statement 2 (MPS2) *Controlling and mitigating the environmental effects mineral extraction in England. Annex 11: Dust* *

THE SCOTTISH OFFICE (1998) Planning Advice Note 50 (PAN50) *Controlling the environmental effects of surface mineral workings. Annex B: The control of dust at surface mineral workings* *

* denotes that a copy of the document is included on the accompanying resource CD

Relevant toolbox talks (refer to Appendix A4)

Spill control

Dust and air quality

Waste management

Storage of waste

Be a good neighbour

Segregation of waste

4.1.8   Legislation

The following table is a brief summary of applicable legislation to dust, emissions and odours, including requirements and divided by UK region. Due to frequent legislative developments users should check <**www.netregs.gov.uk**> when using the table.

Legislation	Key requirements	Direct site requirements	Indirect requirements	Application time planning/during construction/post
England				
Environmental Protection Act 1990 (as amended)	Local authorities can serve an abatement notice upon the cause of a statutory nuisance to stop work immediately	If an abatement notice is served, ensure work ceases immediately and consult with the local authority	Before construction follow best available techniques and consult with all relevant stakeholders if dust emissions or odours are likely to be caused by the processes on site	Planning During construction
Clean Air Act 1993	It is an offence to permit the emission of dark smoke from industrial or trade premises, which is generally enforced by local authorities	Ensure any burning on site is within the exemptions of the regulations	N/A	Planning During construction
Wales				
Environmental Protection Act 1990 (as amended)	Local authorities can serve an abatement notice upon the cause of a statutory nuisance to stop work immediately	If an abatement notice is served, ensure work ceases immediately and consult with the local authority	Before construction follow best available techniques and consult with all relevant stakeholders if dust emissions or odours are likely to be caused by the processes on site	Planning During construction
Clean Air Act 1993	It is an offence to permit the emission of dark smoke from industrial or trade premises, which is generally enforced by local authorities	Ensure any burning on site is within the exemptions of the regulations	N/A	Planning During construction

Scotland

Environmental Protection Act 1990 (as amended)	Local authorities can serve an abatement notice upon the cause of a statutory nuisance to stop work immediately	If an abatement notice is served, ensure work ceases immediately and consult with the local authority	Before construction follow best available techniques and consult with all relevant stakeholders if dust emissions or odours are likely to be caused by the processes on site	Planning During construction
Clean Air Act 1993	It is an offence to permit the emission of dark smoke from industrial or trade premises, which is generally enforced by local authorities	Ensure any burning on site is within the exemptions of the regulations	N/A	Planning During construction

Northern Ireland

Clean Air (Northern Ireland) Order 1981 (as amended)	It is an offence to permit the emission of dark smoke from industrial or trade premises, which is generally enforced by local authorities	Ensure any burning on site is within the exemptions of the regulations	N/A	Planning During construction
Public Health (Ireland) Act 1878	Sets out rules on statutory nuisance, including dirt, rubbish, air pollution and odours, which could lead to the local council or the DoE issuing an abatement notice	If an abatement notice is served, ensure work ceases immediately and consult with the local authority	Before construction follow best available techniques and consult with all relevant stakeholders if dust emissions or odours are likely to be caused by the processes on site	Planning During construction

4.2 Ecology, protected species and habitat

4.2.1 Introduction

Wildlife is the general term given to all of the different species of mammals, birds, fish, insects etc that reside in a specific habitat. Habitat is the term used to describe the characteristics of the area where different species live. This could be, for example, a section of river bank, an area of woodland or even a hedgerow in an inner city park. Ecology is the collective term for all plants (flora) and animals (fauna), their interaction with each other and their dependence on the world around them.

There are several organisations in the UK that have regional responsibility for promoting the conservation of wildlife and natural features:

Conservation body	Contact number
Countryside Council for Wales	0845 1306 229
Defra	08459 335 577
Natural England	01733 455 000
Northern Ireland Environment Agency	0845 302 0008
Scottish Natural Heritage	01463 725 000

Their remit includes providing ecological advice (such as consultation during planning), promoting biodiversity, protecting designated ecological sites, geological and geomorphological sites and protected species. Within each area there are separate bodies that have an environmental remit, but no statutory process. These include county wildlife trusts, and national and local environmental groups such as badger, bat and bird groups (eg the RSPB and WWF).

4.2.2 Why is it important to consider ecology, protected species and habitats?

The natural environment supports all life through interrelated systems that support society in many ways, some that we do not realise and many that are not fully understood by scientists. Ecology has an intrinsic value to society, whether that is part of complex systems that support our lives, or the value it adds on a day to day basis.

Due to past practices and the potential impact that construction has on ecology, the level of protection given to wildlife is increasing through legal controls and contract conditions. The identification wildlife within a site (and surrounding it) needs to be undertaken at the planning stage of a project to ensure the required surveys can be carried out and the correct protection measures can be implemented. This is important so as to avoid both delays to the programme and the extra costs or fines that could be incurred.

Today the public is aware of impacts on the natural environment and the damage that can be caused. Many projects are under the spotlight on environmental grounds and the public will notice poor environmental practice. So it is important for good public relations to have proper regard for ecological issues on site.

Potential impacts on ecology

There are numerous potential impacts that construction sites can have on ecology, but these can be classified in terms of:

- direct impacts on ecology at site level, eg pollution of a watercourse on site, removal of habitat, killing of individual flora or fauna

- indirect impacts occurring because of construction processes/activities, such as deforestation for timber materials, downstream water pollution of a habitat etc.

In many cases, works should avoid disturbance to species during particularly sensitive times, eg hibernation or mating seasons and the bird nesting season. If this is not considered early enough in the project programme, disruption may be caused. When damage has occurred, negotiating with the nature conservation bodies (see Section 4.2.1) and repairing damage takes time, can cause delays to the programme, and will be at the construction company's cost. Consider surveys to be undertaken, consents required and any mitigation requirements early and build these into the project programme to limit disruption.

Managing potential impacts

A responsible attitude should be adopted to ensure construction activities cause the least damage to the surrounding natural environment. Where possible, opportunities should be taken to enhance the natural environment through appropriate habitat creation, which improves biodiversity and promotes positive construction practice.

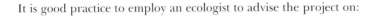

It is good practice to employ an ecologist to advise the project on:

☐ identification of flora and fauna and classification of ecological value of land

☐ developing proposals for mitigation and suitable methods of work to complete it

☐ identifying opportunities for improvements in ecological value during the construction process

☐ legal identification and guidance.

Remember that ecology is a specialised subject, and no two sites are the same, so seek professional advice.

4.2.3 Legal requirements

Disturbing protected species or damaging the places where they live can result in prosecution under a range of legislation. The fine for non-compliance varies according to the species and the habitat and the type of damage caused. For example, if protected species such as bats, badgers, or great crested newts are disturbed, fines may be imposed at £5000 per animal. Also, there is scope for the confiscation of any vehicles or other equipment used to commit the offence.

Contract or planning conditions may state that certain trees must remain undamaged. These trees may be subject to a Tree Preservation Order (TPO), be within a conservation area or related to a former planning permission. Any works that may affect a protected tree should first be approved by the local authority. Replacing damaged mature trees is expensive – a 10 m high tree may cost £2000, plus extra expense for delivery, planting and several years' maintenance.

4.2.4 How to avoid problems

As always, the best thing to do is to prevent problems arising. However, the following are among the signs that there are serious problems on site:

☐ bats or other nocturnal animals being seen during daylight hours or found on the ground near to the site

☐ injured birds, smashed eggs, young unaccompanied fledglings

☐ dead fish floating in watercourse affected by works.

It is necessary to find out whether the client or local planning authority have identified any designated ecological sites or protected species within the local area – check that all relevant information has been passed on to any contractors. Also private developments need to consider the effect they can have on ecology, and identify legal requirements as a minimum.

Usually, particular working practices to protect the ecological features will have been recommended. Where these are given follow the advice. If no recommendations are given, seek advice from head office or the person assigned with environmental responsibility in the site environmental plan, or seek guidance from a professional ecologist.

Before work begins, identify and securely fence off any sensitive habitats and restrict the movement of workers to designated areas. This will help to minimise the damage that may be caused. For many categories of wildlife, for example nesting birds and roosting bats, the timing of work will be important, so correct scheduling may avoid problems (see Table 4.1). Liaise with the nature conservation bodies and with third parties such as local environmental/wildlife groups for advice.

Communicate any areas of concern and license/consent conditions to site personnel, eg induction or toolbox talk training, to ensure they understand the potential issues. As required, adopt a programme of monitoring before and during construction through to site restoration. Ensure that the monitoring process includes action to be taken in the event of problems.

Case study 4.1
Management of swift colony during regeneration
works (courtesy Kier Partnership Homes)

Kier Partnership Homes (KPH) is working to regenerate the Windmill Estate in Fulbourn, Cambridgeshire by demolishing a large number of 1960s houses and replacing them with modern new homes for social landlord Accent Nene. The eaves of the old flat-roofed houses provides extremely attractive nesting sites for swifts that like to breed in inaccessible cavities high up in buildings. Swift numbers in the UK have steadily declined in recent years – partly due to the way new houses are being designed.

To ensure the swifts are not lost from the village, KPH, with guidance from the Swift Conservation organisation and the local authority have provided large numbers of specially-made nesting boxes throughout the new estate. One type is simply fitted to the gable, while another is built into the cavity wall.

A consultant ecologist was employed throughout the summer period to monitor the swifts to discover the size of the colony and the buildings where they nested. This meant KPH could be sure all the birds had safely completed breeding and migrated before they started the second phase of demolitions at the end of the summer.

Wildlife surveys

In some circumstances planning conditions and legislation require surveys of an area to be undertaken to highlight whether there are any protected species of plant or animals in the area that may be affected by the development. A project can be delayed while waiting for the correct time of year to undertake a wildlife survey of the site. Table 4.1 provides an indication of the best time to undertake wildlife surveys before work begins. This should help to minimise the risk of delays. Some surveys may be only carried out at particular times of the year by a professional ecologist.

Notes for Table 4.1

This table is not definitive and is intended to provide an indication only.

The timing of surveys and animal activity will be dependent on factors such as weather conditions.

*   where survey techniques involve the capture, handling or disturbance of protected species then only licensed persons can undertake surveys. Personal survey and monitoring licences are obtained from Natural England, Countryside Council for Wales, Northern Ireland Environment Agency or Scottish Natural Heritage (SNH)

**   where mitigation involves the killing, capture, injury and/or disturbance of protected species and/or the damage, destruction or obstruction of their habitats, a development licence must be obtained from the Department of Environment, Food and Rural Affairs (Defra), the Scottish Government (Environment), Welsh Assembly Government (Countryside Division) or the Northern Ireland Environment Agency. Licences will be granted only to persons who have proven competence in dealing with the species concerned. Development licence applications take about 30 days to be processed by government departments. Where mitigation works need to be conducted under licence before works begin, licence applications will need to be submitted considerably earlier

***   where mitigation involves the capture of white-clawed crayfish, a mitigation licence must be obtained from Natural England, Countryside Council for Wales, Northern Ireland Environment Agency or Scottish Natural Heritage. Licences will be granted only to persons who have proven competence in dealing with the species concerned

1   Applies in Northern Ireland only

Key	
	Recommended survey time
	No surveys
	Mitigation conducted at these times
	Mitigation works restricted

		Licence required?	J	F	M	A	M	J	J	A	S	O	N	D
Habitats/ vegetation	Surveys	N	Mosses and lichens. No other detailed plant surveys – Phase 1 surveys only (least suitable time)			Detailed habitat assessment surveys. Surveys for higher plants and ferns. Mosses and lichens in April, May and September only							Mosses and lichens. No other detailed plant surveys – Phase 1 surveys only (least suitable time)	
	Mitigation	N	Planting and translocation		No mitigation for majority of species							Planting and translocation		
Birds	Surveys	N	Winter birds			Breeding birds/ migrant species		Breeding birds			Breeding birds/ migrant species		Winter birds	
	Mitigation		Clearance works may be conducted at this time, but must stop immediately if any nesting birds are found			No clearance or construction works. Bird nesting season					Clearance works may be conducted at this me, but must stop immediately if any nesting birds are found			
Badgers	Surveys	*	All survey methods – best time is in spring and early autumn/winter											
	Mitigation	**	Building of artificial setts. No disturbance of existing setts				Stopping up or destruction of existing setts							See Jan to June
Bats	Surveys	*	Inspection of hibernation, tree and building roosts			No surveys	Activity surveys and inspection of building roosts. Emergence counts.					No surveys	Inspection of hibernation, tree and building roosts	
	Mitigation	**	Works on maternity roosts only		Works on maternity roosts until mid-May. Works on hibernation roosts from mid-March		Works on hibernation roosts only				Hibernation roosts until November. Maternity roosts from mid-September		Works on maternity roosts only	

Table 4.1 Guidance on the optimal timing for carrying out specialist ecological surveys and mitigation

		Licence required?	J	F	M	A	M	J	J	A	S	O	N	D
Dormice	Surveys	*	Nut searches (sub-optimum time)	Nut searches (sub-optimum time)	Nest searches (April sub-optimum time)	Nest searches (April sub-optimum time)	Cage traps and hair tube surveys to mid-October. Nut searches from September (optimum time September to December). Nest searches (optimum time: September to March)						Nut searches and nest searches (optimum time)	Nut searches and nest searches (optimum time)
	Mitigation	**	No clearance works	No clearance works	No clearance works	No clearance works	Clearance works (sub-optimum time)	No clearance works	No clearance works	No clearance works	Clearance works to early October (optimum time)	Clearance works to early October (optimum time)	No clearance works	No clearance works
Otters	Surveys	*	Surveys for otters can potentially be conducted all year round, though vegetation cover and weather conditions may limit the times at which surveys can be carried out											
	Mitigation	**	Mitigation can potentially be conducted in any month, but is likely to be restricted where otters are found to be breeding											
Pine martens	Surveys	*	Surveys may be conducted all year round weather permitting. Optimum time is spring and summer. Surveys for breeding dens from March to May.											
	Mitigation	**	Works in areas of pine marten habitat and dens	Works in areas of pine marten habitat and dens	Avoid all works in pine marten habitat								Works in areas of pine marten habitat and dens	Works in areas of pine marten habitat and dens
Red squirrels	Surveys	*	Surveys may be conducted all year round weather permitting. Surveys for breeding females from December to September. Optimum time is spring and summer.											
	Mitigation	**			Avoid all works in red squirrel habitat							Works should preferably be conducted at this time	Works should preferably be conducted at this time	Avoid all works in red squirrel habitat

Table 4.1 (contd)   Guidance on the optimal timing for carrying out specialist ecological surveys and mitigation

Taxon		Licence required?	J	F	M	A	M	J	J	A	S	O	N	D
Water voles (n/a in NI)	Surveys	*	Reduced activity	Initial surveys possible	All survey methods can be used during this period, though vegetation cover and weather conditions may limit the times at which surveys can be carried out. Optimum time: March to June								Initial surveys possible	Reduced activity
	Mitigation	N²	Avoid all works in water vole habitat			Works in water voles habitat possible	Avoid all works in water vole habitat				Works in water vole habitat possible		Avoid all works in water vole habitat	
Sand lizards, smooth snakes (n/a in NI)¹ **and common lizards**	Surveys	*	No surveys – reptiles in hibernation		Activity surveys from March to June and in September/October. Surveys are limited by high temperatures during July and August. Peak survey months are April, May and September								No surveys – reptiles in hibernation	
	Mitigation	**	Scrub clearance		Capture and translocation programmes can only be conducted while reptiles are active (March to June and September/October). Trapping is limited by high temperatures during July/August. Scrub clearance								Scrub clearance	
Other reptiles	Surveys	N	No surveys – reptiles in hibernation		Activity surveys from March to June and in September/October. Surveys are limited by high temperatures during July and August. Peak survey months are April, May and September								No surveys – reptiles in hibernation	
	Mitigation	N	Scrub clearance		Capture and translocation programmes can only be conducted whilst reptiles are active (March to June and September/October). Trapping is limited by high temperatures during July/August. Scrub clearance								Scrub clearance	

Table 4.1 (contd)   Guidance on the optimal timing for carrying out specialist ecological surveys and mitigation

	Licence required?	J	F	M	A	M	J	J	A	S	O	N	D
Great crested newts (n/a in NI) — Surveys	*	No surveys – newts in hibernation	No surveys – newts in hibernation	Pond surveys for adults: mid-March to mid-June. Surveys must include visits undertaken between mid-April and mid-May. Egg surveys April to mid-May. Larvae surveys from mid-June. Terrestrial habitat surveys				Larvae surveys to mid-August Terrestrial habitat surveys		Terrestrial habitat surveys		No surveys – newts in hibernation	
Great crested newts — Mitigation	**	No trapping of newts Pond management only	No trapping of newts Pond management only	Newt trapping programmes in ponds and on land				Newt trapping on land only				No trapping of newts Pond management only	
Natterjack toads — Surveys	*	No surveys - toads in hibernation	No surveys - toads in hibernation		Surveys of breeding ponds for adults				Surveys for adults on land			No surveys - toads in hibernation	
Natterjack toads — Mitigation	**	Pond management works	Pond management works		Surveys for tadpoles from May onwards. Surveys for adults on land. Trapping of adults in ponds from April to July. Trapping of adults on land. Trapping of tadpoles from May to early September						Pond management works	Pond management works	

Table 4.1 (contd)   Guidance on the optimal timing for carrying out specialist ecological surveys and mitigation

		Licence required?	J	F	M	A	M	J	J	A	S	O	N	D
White-clawed crayfish	Surveys	*	Reduced activity	Reduced activity	Reduced activity	Surveys can be undertaken	Avoid surveys (females are releasing young)	Optimum time for surveys	Optimum time for surveys	Optimum time for surveys	Optimum time for surveys	Optimum time for surveys	Reduced activity	Reduced activity
White-clawed crayfish	Mitigation	***	Avoid capture programmes (low activity levels may lead to animals being easily missed)	Avoid capture programmes (low activity levels may lead to animals being easily missed)	Avoid capture programmes (low activity levels may lead to animals being easily missed)	Exclusion of crayfish from construction areas	Avoid capture programmes	Exclusion of crayfish from construction areas	Exclusion of crayfish from construction areas	Exclusion of crayfish from construction areas	Exclusion of crayfish from construction areas	Exclusion of crayfish from construction areas	Avoid capture programmes (low activity levels may lead to animals being easily missed)	Avoid capture programmes (low activity levels may lead to animals being easily missed)
Fish	Surveys	*	For coastal, river and stream-dwelling species, the timing of surveys will depend on the migration pattern of the species concerned. Where surveys require information on breeding, the timing of surveys will need to coincide with the breeding period, which may be summer or winter months, depending on the species											
Fish	Mitigation	**	Mitigation for the protection of watercourses is required at all times of year. Mitigation for particular fish species will need to be timed so as to avoid the breeding season. This varies from species to species											

Table 4.1 (contd)   Guidance on the optimal timing for carrying out specialist ecological surveys and mitigation

Important considerations

There are two ways in which ecological issues have to be considered on site:

1   Where species or areas of the site have been identified for particular protection

    This may have been highlighted through site surveys and studies carried out by an experienced consultant, or through the fact that the site is identified on the local biodiversity plan or the site has a special designation (for example a nature reserve). Site staff should be made aware of the special working methods that they should follow to protect any sensitive species or habitats and of any areas or features that should be avoided by traffic movements, materials storage or other impacts from the site.

2   Where protected species are discovered when the contractor is already on site and works have begun

    Work should be stopped immediately, and the site manager should seek expert advice on how to proceed. Consultation with the nature conservation bodies may have to take place to discuss the best way to continue.

To minimise general damage to ecology on site

Those working in construction should take all possible steps to avoid impacts on wildlife and habitats and to protect particular species and designated sites. It is important to take a responsible attitude to the natural environment as a whole. Be aware that most activities during construction can have a direct, temporary or permanent impact on the surrounding ecology, such as:

☐   changes to water quality

☐   the destruction of places inhabited by plants and animals (this is a feature of most developments)

☐   interruptions to the movement of wildlife

☐   habitat fragmentation or vegetation damage

☐   removal of hedgerows and other vegetation, which may require legal consent

☐   high noise levels disturbing nearby ecology

☐ changes in lighting

☐ damage, removal or burial of important rock formations or landforms

☐ dust generation that may affect protected plant species

☐ silt and soil run-off that may affect plant species, which may affect the animals that depend on them.

Also, be aware that works on site may affect ecological resources off-site and consideration should be given to the surrounding area and any protective or preventative measures that should be implemented. For example, it is an offence to disturb nesting birds next to a site.

4.2.5 Dealing with protected species

Many animals, plants and birds are protected throughout or for part of the year under the Wildlife and Countryside Act 1981 (as amended), The Wildlife (Northern Ireland) Order 1985 and The Nature Conservation (Scotland) Act, 2004. Work may have to be adapted or delayed until such a time that the development will cause no adverse effect on them or the places where they live. Work may be subject to licenses issued by the nature conservation bodies or Defra if it is considered that the planned activities could affect protected species or habitats. These organisations should be consulted for advice before works start to avoid potentially expensive delays.

To obtain a full list of species protected under the Wildlife and Countryside Act 1981 (as amended) contact the relevant nature conservation body. To assist dealing with them on site refer to CIRIA's forthcoming wildlife guidance publication (C691, 2011). If it is suspected that any protected animal may be affected by the site works stop and seek specialist advice before continuing.

Note that different regions operate different schedules of protected species through their respective legislation.

In Scotland licences to disturb European protected species are issued by the Scottish Government Rural Directorate. Licences to disturb badgers are issued by Scottish Natural Heritage (SNH).

Some of the important species that may be encountered are as follows.

Bats

Bats roost in a variety of localities in both urban and rural areas, these include:

☐ holes and cracks in trees

☐ in roofs and walls of buildings

☐ under bridges

☐ underground caves

☐ disused railway tunnels.

Bats hibernate between October and April and breed between May and September. If bats are likely to be encountered, a survey will be required by a suitably licensed ecologist to establish the location and size of the roost. Only suitably licensed ecologists are allowed legally to enter known bat roosts or to capture or handle bats. It is illegal to injure, kill, capture or disturb a bat, or to damage trees, buildings or other places used for roosting, even if the roost is unoccupied at the time.

Building developer PJ Livesey Group was fined £3500 and ordered to pay costs of £2000 after it proceeded with unlicensed alterations to a Victorian mansion that destroyed a bat roost.

Badgers

Badgers and their setts are protected under the Protection of Badgers Act 1992. It is an offence to directly disturb a badger sett, or to carry out works close to a badger sett that could cause a disturbance, without a licence from the relevant nature conservation body or consent from Defra. Badgers are widespread throughout the UK and can be found living in:

☐ woodland

☐ road and railway embankments

☐ refuse tips

☐ under buildings

☐ in hollow trees.

Setts are a network of tunnels and chambers underground. The entrance is visible above ground and can be identified by a rounded or flattened, oval-shaped hole and the presence of large spoil mounds.

Badger licences should be obtained from the relevant statutory nature conservation organisation (SNCO), Natural England, SNH, CCW or NIEA, if site activity is likely to interfere with a badger sett for example:

☐ damaging or destroying a badger sett

☐ obstructing any entrance to a sett

☐ disturbing a badger when it is occupying a sett.

If a badger or a sett is discovered after works have started, work must stop immediately and expert advice must be sought.

Foxes

Foxes occur in nearly all habitats and are well adapted to living in built-up areas, often being seen in town centres and gardens. Foxes are active all year round (less so during winter) and can be seen at any time of the day. Breeding occurs during spring. Foxes occupy underground dens called "earths". Be aware that a licence is required for badger setts even if occupied by foxes.

Cruelty to and trapping of foxes is illegal. Fox earths should not be destroyed until it is certain that they are unoccupied. Holes should not be filled between March and May as cubs are likely to be below ground. If a fox earth is discovered after works have started, work must stop immediately and expert advice must be sought before undertaking any further works.

Water voles

Water voles often are confused with rats. Water voles can be found in shallow burrows, often close to the ground surface, which can extend up to 5 m from the water edge near or below the water-line in various localities. There should be no construction works or equipment within 5 m of a watercourse, including cabins and plant – especially generator sets as the vibrations caused by these can lead to disturbance through the ground.

Water voles may be found in the banks adjacent to:

☐ slow-flowing rivers

☐ streams

☐ ditches

☐   dykes

☐   around ponds and lakes.

Water voles tend to be more active during the day and are active all year round. Water voles and their burrows are legally protected against damage and disturbance. If water voles are found after works have started, all works must stop immediately to avoid breaking the law, and expert advice must be sought.

A landowner in Carmarthenshire was fined £1500 and ordered to pay £1000 in legal costs for destroying a water vole habitat during the development of a golf course. This was in contravention of the planning conditions that had been imposed to ensure their protection.

Reptiles

All reptiles are protected and should not be killed or injured. In the UK there are six native species of land-dwelling reptiles:

☐   common lizard

☐   sand lizard

☐   slow-worm

☐   adder

☐   grass snake

☐   smooth snake.

Reptiles hibernate in winter but are active the rest of the year. Mating takes place between April and June and the young are born between July and October. Reptiles can be found throughout the UK and are typically found in dense grassland, or scrub with open areas where they can bask, among vegetation on railway embankments and hedgerows. They can also be found sheltering under rocks and logs. It is illegal to kill or injure common lizards, slow-worms, grass snakes and adders. Any works affecting sand lizards and smooth snakes are illegal without a licence. If reptiles are found, or are likely to be found, stop work immediately and seek advice from an expert.

Amphibians

Great Crested Newts (see Figure 4.3) and Natterjack Toads (see Figure 4.4) are fully protected by law. Natterjack Toads are extremely rare in Britain. To kill, injure or disturb them or their habitat, is an offence. If found or suspected on site all works must stop immediately and expert advice sought.

*Figure 4.3
Great Crested
Newt (courtesy
Scottish Natural
Heritage)*

*Figure 4.4
Natterjack toad*

Great Crested Newts can be found predominantly in ponds in rural, urban and suburban areas. Great Crested Newts are nocturnal and spend most of their time within grass, scrub, woodland and under logs within 500 m of a water body. They spawn in ponds and slow moving water bodies between March and June. Other species of newt that could be encountered on site are the smooth (see Figure 4.5) or palmate (see Figure 4.6).

Figure 4.5
Smooth newt

Figure 4.6
Palmate newt (courtesy
Scottish Natural Heritage)

Nesting birds

All birds and their nests are protected under Part 1 of the Wildlife and Countryside Act 1981 (and amendments), with some rare species, eg Barn Owl, birds of prey and Kingfishers, carrying further protection against disturbance. To avoid disturbance to nesting birds, the programming of tree and hedge removal should fall outside of the nesting season (March to the end of July).

Birds often use building sites as breeding areas including nesting on scaffolding or machinery. If this occurs the equipment cannot be used until the birds have finished nesting and any young have left the nest. Also, the area may need to be sealed off to prevent any disturbance. If nesting birds are found, consult the nature conservation bodies for further advice.

4.2.6 Noxious and invasive plants

Noxious plants are those that can pose a risk to human or environmental health because of the chemicals they contain. Care should be taken when in contact with such plants or when removing them from site.

Invasive species are those that are not native to the UK and have been introduced into our environment. Often invasive species out-compete native species due to lack of natural controls and do not support wildlife habitats. Invasive species are a complex issue affecting regions throughout the UK, for further information see Booy *et al* (2008) and/or guidance on Japanese Knotweed by the Environment Agency (2006).

Ecology is adversely affected through the spreading of noxious and invasive plants, and it is an offence to cause their spread. These plants are covered by Schedule 9 of the Wildlife and Countryside Act 1981 (as amended) or under the Weeds Act 1959 (as amended), Noxious Weeds (Northern Ireland) Order 1977. Note that species may be added to the list so it is important to keep up-to-date.

If noxious or invasive plants are found on site it is the responsibility of the site manager to take the following action:

☐ cordon off the area to prevent any inadvertent spreading

☐ notify the environmental regulator that the plant is present

☐ ensure any vehicles that have been in the affected area have their wheels/tracks thoroughly washed before leaving the area of the site where the plant is located. Water, including material, used to clean vehicles must be controlled to prevent the spread of the plant (through seeds etc).

Seek specialist advice for the most effective treatment of the plant to prevent spreading, giving the particular circumstances on site.

Example: invasive plant species

☐ Japanese Knotweed grows densely, shades out other plants, reduces biodiversity, and penetrates asphalt, walls, and foundations. It is a destructive plant that has been known to re-grow through tarmac and paving as well as disrupting underground structures and services.

☐ Giant Hogweed has poisonous sap and extreme care should be taken when removing such a species. Relevant personal protective equipment (PPE) should be provided as the sap can burn and irritate skin. Appropriate PPE should be provided if there is any chance of the sap being spread or vaporised through cutting.

☐ Ragwort is poisonous to sheep, horses etc.

☐ Thistle shades out other plants and reduces biodiversity.

☐ Himalayan Balsam grows densely along river banks and in wetland areas, shades out other plants, and reduces biodiversity. It should be cut down when in flower to prevent the seed heads from forming and spraying their seeds further infesting the local area.

For more information refer to Booy et al (2008)

Figure 4.7
Installation of a Japanese knotweed rhizome barrier

Following specialist advice approval for the proposed control methods should be sought from the environmental regulator.

4.2.7 Habitats

Habitat can be defined as an area possessing uniformity of landform, vegetation, climate or any other quality assumed to be important. Usually, in terms of site assessment and management, it is uniformity of vegetation that characterises a habitat. Habitats are usually formed naturally although some can be man-made (eg through translocation). There are several types of habitat:

☐ coastal and marine

☐ grassland

☐ heathland

☐ hedgerows and individual trees

☐ road and railway embankments

☐ soil

☐ urban areas

☐ wetland

☐ woodland and scrub.

The ecological richness of a habitat (its biodiversity) can be affected in a number of ways. Invasive plants such as Japanese Knotweed can reduce biodiversity through out-competing other plant species. The effect of human activities on habitats include spillages of hazardous substances on the ground and into water, felling trees or removing hedgerows, site clearance or demolition.

Measures to reinstate any habitats damaged during the works may form part of the contract or planning conditions. Such measures have to be planned in advance and may require specialist advice. There may be particular requirements in selecting the type of species for reinstating.

Translocation of species

Translocation should be considered as the last resort and only occur when habitat damage is anticipated and unavoidable, but the species concerned can be moved off the site and reinstated elsewhere. Where translocation is required this typically forms part of the site preparation works and is carried out by specialists. Translocation often needs to take place within specific time periods (refer to Table 4.1), and may influence the project programme. Both aftercare and monitoring of translocated species are essential. Various acts concerning animal welfare legislation may apply (for example the Animal Welfare Act 2006).Without planning and consideration, translocation may become an expensive process. For more information refer to CIRIA C600 and C601 (Anderson and Groutage, 2003).

Figure 4.8
Badger sett
construction
(courtesy Kier)

4.2.8   Natural features

Designated sites

Sites with important ecological attributes (including plant and animal species) or natural landforms can be given special protection that can be applied at the regional, national or international level according to their importance or rarity. Examples of designated sites (in alphabetical order) are:

☐   area of outstanding natural beauty (AONB)

☐   county wildlife sites (CWS)

☐   local nature reserve (LNR)

☐   national nature reserve (NNR)

- □ special area of conservation (SAC)
- □ special protection area (SPA)
- □ site of importance for nature conservation (SINC)
- □ site of nature conservation interest (SNCI)
- □ site of special scientific interest (SSSI) or area of special scientific interest (ASSI)
- □ RAMSAR (wetlands of international importance)
- □ regionally important geological sites (RIGS)
- □ world heritage sites (WHS).

Always contact the nature conservation body for further guidance on designated sites.

It is an offence to carry out works on a designated site without the permission of the relevant nature conservation body. Often several months' notice is required before works begin. It is important to adhere to working methods once they have been agreed with the nature conservation bodies.

Trees and hedgerows

Damage to trees and hedgerows may be caused either through direct physical injury to the branches, trunk or roots or by changing the soil or water character around the roots. This can arise from various actions including compaction (even one piece of machinery going over the roots can cause damage), raising soil levels, impervious covering around tree roots, raising the water table, hazardous spillages, soil stripping, or excavations. Refer to the checklist at the end of this section for more details (see also BS 5837:2005).

West Midland Safari park was fined £7500 and forced to pay legal costs in excess of £12 000 after cutting down protected trees without council consent for the construction of their new wild river rafting ride.

Tree protection

A tree protection order (TPO) protects a single tree, group of trees or woodland. It protects trees from being topped, lopped or removed. Consent must be obtained before any work on a tree with a TPO is undertaken. Failure to gain permission is an offence and could result in a fine of up to £20 000. All trees located within a conservation area are protected.

The local authority planning department should be contacted before work starts on any protected trees. The procedure to gain permission to work on a tree(s) with a TPO involves:

☐ obtain the relevant form from the local authority

☐ fill out the form outlining the intended work

☐ return the completed form to the local authority

☐ the local authority has up to two months to make a decision (local residents are able to appeal against the work during this time).

When a tree that has a TPO in force is dead, dying or dangerous, it can be felled without permission, but the local authority should always be consulted before any action is taken.

Before removing any trees on local authority land, the relevant authority needs to be contacted so that they can identify whether there is a need to place a provisional TPO on any of the tree(s) that may otherwise be damaged or removed during construction works.

Figure 4.9
Tree protection (courtesy Kier)

Hedgerow protection

Hedgerows in England and Wales are protected under the Hedgerow Regulations 1997, which make it a legal requirement to notify the local planning authority (LPA) in whose area the hedgerow is situated. Under these regulations the removal of any hedge longer then 20 m, requires planning permission. If the hedge is shown to be significant in terms of its age, environmental or historical importance, then the planning authority can refuse such permission (after a six week determination period) and take further measures to protect the hedgerow. In Scotland restrictions may be detailed during planning under the Town and County Planning (Scotland) Act 1997.

Rocks and landforms

These are an important part of our natural heritage. Some rock exposures and landforms will be SSSIs/ASSIs, but others may be locally important. If there is any doubt as to the importance of these features and how to protect them, contact the nature conservation bodies who will provide contact details for a local RIGS group.

4.2.9   Good practice checklists

 What to look out for on site

Protected species

- ☐ if found on site (or suspected to be on site) follow the required processes to manage them
- ☐ consult site ecologist before any works to mitigate or translocate are undertaken

Invasive species

- ☐ if found on site (or suspected to be on site) follow the required processes to manage them
- ☐ seek expert advice before any works are undertaken

Nesting birds

- ☐ if found, do not disturb or cut down trees or shrubs
- ☐ to avoid accidental disturbance do not fell or clear any trees or shrubs between March and August

Trees

- ☐ check whether any trees on site are covered by a tree preservation order and liaise with local authority (local planning office in Northern Ireland)

Working near water

Place a protective bund around ponds to prevent water pollution

Dewatering can affect the ecology of wetlands around the site. Consider monitoring water levels during the works

Avoiding damage to trees and hedgerows

Keep vehicles and plant away from them

Put up temporary fencing to mark out area around those that need to be protected

Do not cut or damage any roots greater than 25 mm in diameter within the protected area

Cut roots only with a clean hand saw, not a spade or mechanical digger

What to look out for on site

Wrap damp sacking around any exposed roots until ready for backfilling	
Backfill holes with care, to ensure that roots are not damaged, and compact backfill lightly	
Do not store spoil or building materials within protected area or under tree canopy	
Keep toxic materials such as diesel and cement well away	
Always avoid damaging bark or branches	

4.2.10   Further guidance

Protected species

Amphibians

BEEBEE, T and DENTON, J (1996) *Natterjack toad conservation handbook*, English Nature, Peterborough (ISBN: 1-85716-220-X) *

ENGLISH NATURE (2001) *Great crested newts – mititgation guidelines*, English Nature, Peterborough (ISBN: 1-85716-568-3) *

LANGTON, T, BECKETT, C and FOSTER, J (2001) *Great crested newt conservation handbook*, Froglife, Halesworth, Suffolk (ISBN: 0-95211-064-4) *

Mammals

BAT CONSERVATION TRUST (2007) *Bat surveys – good practice guidelines*, Bat Conservation Trust, London *

COUNTRYSIDE COUNCIL FOR WALES (2009) *Water voles and development*, Countryside Council for Wales, Gwynedd *

ENVIRONMENT AND HERITAGE SERVICE (2004) *Badgers and development*, Northern Ireland Environment Agency, Belfast (ISBN: 1-90512-705-7) *

MITCHELL-JONES, A J (2004) *Bat mitigation guidelines*, English Nature, Peterborough (ISBN: 1-85716-781-3) *

NATURAL ENGLAND (2008) *Water voles and development: licensing policy*, TIN042, Natural England, Peterborough *

NATURAL ENGLAND (2009) *Badgers and development – a guide to best practice and licensing*, interim guidance document, Natural England, Sheffield *

NEWTON, J, NICHOLSON, B and SAUNDERS, R (eds) (2011) *Working with wildlife: guidance for the construction industry*, C691 CIRIA, London (ISBN: 978-0-86017-691-6)

SCOTTISH NATURAL HERITAGE (2001) *Badgers and development*, NP4K0601, Scottish Natural Heritage, Perth, Scotland (ISBN 1 85397 1375) *

WARD, D, HOLMES, N and JOSE, P (eds) (1994) *The new rivers and wildlife handbook*, The Royal Society for the Protection of Birds, UK (ISBN: 978-0-90313-870-3)

Reptiles

ENGLISH NATURE (2004) *Reptiles: guidelines for developers*, English Nature, Peterborough (ISBN: 1-85716-807-0) *

Noxious and invasive plants

BOOY, O, WADE, M and WHITE, V (2008) *Invasive species management for infrastructure managers and the construction industry*, CIRIA, C679, CIRIA, London (ISBN: 978-0-86017-879-4)

ENVIRONMENT AGENCY (2006) *Managing Japanese Knotweed on development sites – The Knotweed Code of Practice*, Environment Agency, Bristol *

SEPA (2008) *Onsite management of Japanese Knotweed and associated contaminated soils*, Technical Guidance Note, Scottish Environment Protection Agency, Stirling *

Habitats

ANDERSON, P and GROUTAGE, P (2003) *Habitats translocation – a best practice guide*, C600, CIRIA, London (ISBN: 978-0-86017-600-8)

ANDERSON, P and GROUTAGE, P (2003) *A review of habitat translocation*, C601CD, CIRIA, London (ISBN: 978-0-86017-601-5)

CLG (2005) Planning Policy Statement (PPS) 9 *Biodiversity and geological conservation*, Communities And Local GovernmenT, London (ISBN: 978-0-11753-954-9) *

British Standards

BS 5837:2005 *Trees in relation to construction. Recommendations*

*   denotes that a copy of the document is included on the accompanying resource CD

| Relevant toolbox talks (refer to Appendix A4) |
| Spill control |
| Water pollution prevention (fuel and oil) |
| Noise and vibration |
| Water pollution: silt |
| Water pollution: cement and concrete |
| Tree protection |
| Japanese Knotweed |
| Himalayan Balsam |
| Giant Hogweed |
| Pumping and overpumping |
| Washing down plant and machinery |
| Bats |
| Badgers |
| Great crested newts |
| Working on previously developed land |

4.2.11 Legislation

The following table is a brief summary of applicable legislation on ecology, protected species and habitats, including requirements and divided by UK region. Due to frequent legislative developments users should check <www.netregs.gov.uk> when using the table.

Legislation	Key requirements	Direct site requirements	Indirect requirements	Application time planning/during construction/post
England				
Wildlife & Countryside Act 1981 (as amended)	This Act (as amended) is the major legal instrument for wildlife protection in Britain. It is divided into four parts covering protection of wildlife, designation of protected areas, public rights of way, and miscellaneous provisions. It sets out the system to define and control SSSIs and the best examples of natural heritage of wildlife habitats, geological features and landforms. It also makes provisions for the protection of land from weeds such as Japanese Knotweed (see Weeds Act 1959), and lists species protected from disturbance, injury, intentional destruction or sale, eg nesting birds	Any activities that may impact upon birds, animals, plants or invasive plants should be undertaken in line with the guidance set out in this Act. The Act also provides for the notification of SSSIs and any works being undertaken on them	N/A	Planning During construction
The Conservation (Natural Habitats, &c.) Regulations 1994	Allows for the designation of SACs, and SPAs, collectively known as "European Sites". All the protected species listed on the schedules of the Regulations are also listed within the Wildlife & Countryside Act 1981 (as amended)	Any activities undertaken that may affect a protected habitat listed under these Regulations should be discussed with the relevant local authority and Natural England before work starts	N/A	Planning During construction

Legislation	Key requirements	Direct site requirements	Indirect requirements	Application time planning/during construction/post
The Environmental Damage (Prevention and Remediation) Regulations 2009	Any environmental damage following activity on site should be remedied. If there is a risk of damage from any business activities, it must be prevented. The Regulations do not apply to environmental damage caused before the regulations came into force. Overall, the Regulations are likely to be used only for the most serious cases of damage. Under the Regulations, environmental damage is: □ serious damage to surface or groundwater □ contamination of land where there is a significant risk to human health □ serious damage to EU protected natural habitats and species or damage to SSSIs	If any activity threatens to cause, or has caused, environmental damage then: □ take steps to prevent the damage (or further damage) occurring □ inform the Environment Agency or other authorities who will provide information on how to prevent and/or remedy the damage. If the Environment Agency or another authority has to remedy the damage then the company will have to pay the costs	N/A	Planning During construction Post construction

Legislation	Key requirements	Direct site requirements	Indirect requirements	Application time planning/during construction/post
Protection of Badgers Act 1992	The Act makes it an offence to: 1 Kill, injure or take a badger. 2 Cruelly ill-treat any badger. 3 Interfere with a badger sett.	If a site contains signs of badger activity (ie establishment of a sett) an ecologist should be consulted to assess the site If known badger setts are within the site or will be disturbed by the activities of the site a license must be sought from Natural England	N/A	Planning During construction
Hedgerow Regulations 1997	To be protected, the hedgerow must: ☐ run on agricultural land or common land, for example a village green, or land that runs alongside it. Garden hedges are not protected ☐ be on or bordering a nature reserve, or SSSI ☐ be at least 30 years old and at least 20 m long	If a protected hedgerow will be affected by site works then permission to remove the hedgerow will need to be sought from the local planning authority	N/A	Planning During construction

Legislation	Key requirements	Direct site requirements	Indirect requirements	Application time planning/during construction/post
Town and Country Planning (Trees) Regulations 1999 (as amended)	These regulations make provision for the protection of trees. Features include: ☐ powers for local authorities to assign TPO status to single or groups of trees ☐ local authorities have powers to vary and revoke TPOs ☐ the regulations provide for circumstances when trees protected by TPOs can be topped, lopped or felled	Adhere to any TPOs served by the local authority. Do not damage or remove trees without first consulting the local authority	N/A	Planning During construction
Weed Act 1959 (as amended)	Requires the occupiers of land on which injurious weeds are growing to take action to prevent the spread of such weeds. The Act specifies five such species: Common Ragwort, Spear thistle, Creeping Field thistle, Broad leaved dock and Curled dock	If injurious weeds are found on site guidance should be sought from Defra	N/A	Planning During construction

Legislation	Key requirements	Direct site requirements	Indirect requirements	Application time planning/during construction/post
Wales				
Wildlife & Countryside Act 1981 (as amended)	This Act (as amended) is the major legal instrument for wildlife protection in Britain. It is divided into four parts covering protection of wildlife, designation of protected areas, public rights of way, and miscellaneous provisions. It sets out the system to define and control SSSIs and the best examples of natural heritage of wildlife habitats, geological features and landforms. It also makes provisions for the protection of land from weeds such as Japanese Knotweed (see Weeds Act 1959), and lists species protected from disturbance, injury, intentional destruction or sale, eg nesting birds	Any activities that may impact upon birds, animals, plants or invasive plants should be undertaken in-line with the guidance set out in this Act. The Act also provides for the notification of SSSIs and any works being undertaken on them	N/A	Planning During construction
The Conservation (Natural Habitats, &c.) Regulations 1994	Allows for the designation of SACs, and SPAs, collectively known as "European sites". All the protected species listed on the schedules of the Regulations are also listed within the Wildlife & Countryside Act 1981 (as amended)	Any activities undertaken that may affect a protected habitat listed under these Regulations should be discussed with the relevant local authority and Natural England before work starts	N/A	Planning During construction

Legislation	Key requirements	Direct site requirements	Indirect requirements	Application time planning/during construction/post
The Conservation (Natural Habitats, &c.) Regulations 1994	Allows for the designation of SACs, and SPAs, collectively known as "European sites". All the protected species listed on the schedules of the Regulations are also listed within the Wildlife & Countryside Act 1981 (as amended)	Any activities undertaken that may affect a protected habitat listed under these regulations should be discussed with the relevant local authority and CCW before work starts	N/A	Planning During construction
Environmental Damage (Prevention and Remediation) (Wales) Regulations 2009	If any business activities cause environmental damage then it should be remedied. If there is a risk of damage from business activities then it must be prevented The regulations do not apply to environmental damage caused before the regulations came into force Overall, the Regulations are likely to be used only for the most serious cases of damage Under the Regulations, environmental damage is: ☐ serious damage to surface or groundwater ☐ contamination of land where there is a significant risk to human health ☐ serious damage to EU protected natural habitats and species or damage to SSSIs	If any activities threaten to cause, or have caused, environmental damage then: ☐ take steps to prevent the damage (or further damage) occurring ☐ inform the Environment Agency or other authorities who will provide information on how to prevent and/or remedy the damage If the Environment Agency has to remedy the damage, then the company will have to pay the costs	N/A	Planning During construction Post construction

Legislation	Key requirements	Direct site requirements	Indirect requirements	Application time planning/during construction/post
Protection of Badgers Act 1992	The Act makes it an offence to: 1 Kill, injure or take a badger. 2 Cruelly ill-treat any badger. 3 Interfere with a badger sett.	If a site contains signs of badger activity an ecologist should be consulted to assess the site If known badger setts are within the site or will be disturbed by the activities of the site a license must be sought from CCW	N/A	Planning During construction
Hedgerow Regulations 1997	To be protected, the hedgerow must: ☐ run on agricultural land or common land, for example a village green, or land that runs alongside it. Garden hedges are not protected ☐ be on or bordering a nature reserve, or SSSI ☐ be at least 30 years old and at least 20 m long	If a protected hedgerow will be affected by site works then permission to remove the hedgerow will need to be sought from the local authority	N/A	Planning During construction
Town and Country Planning (Trees) Regulations 1999 (as amended)	These Regulations make provision for the protection of trees. Features include: ☐ provides power for local authorities to assign TPO) status to single or groups of trees ☐ local authorities have powers to vary and revoke TPOs ☐ the regulation also provides for circumstances when trees protected by TPOs can be topped, lopped or felled	Adhere to any TPOs served by the local authority. Do not damage or remove trees without first consulting the local authority	N/A	Planning During construction

Legislation	Key requirements	Direct site requirements	Indirect requirements	Application time planning/during construction/post
Weed Act 1959 (as amended)	Requires the occupiers of land on which injurious weeds are growing to take action to prevent the spread of such weeds. The Act specifies five such species: Common Ragwort, Spear thistle, Creeping Field thistle, Broad leaved dock and Curled dock	If injurious weeds are found on site guidance should be sought from Defra	N/A	Planning During construction
Scotland				
Environmental Liability (Scotland) Regulations 2009 SSI 266	If any business activities cause environmental damage then it should be remedied. If there is a risk of damage from business activities then it must be prevented The Regulations do not apply to environmental damage caused before the Regulations came into force Overall, the Regulations are likely to be used only for the most serious cases of damage Under the Regulations, environmental damage is: ☐ serious damage to surface or groundwater ☐ contamination of land where there is a significant risk to human health ☐ serious damage to EU protected natural habitats and species or damage to SSSIs	If any activities threaten to cause, or have caused, environmental damage then: ☐ take steps to prevent the damage (or further damage) occurring ☐ inform SEPA or other authorities who will provide information on how to prevent and/or remedy the damage If SEPA has to remedy the damage, then the company will have to pay the costs	N/A	Planning During construction Post construction

Legislation	Key requirements	Direct site requirements	Indirect requirements	Application time planning/during construction/post
The Nature Conservation (Scotland) Act, 2004	This Act (as amended) sets out the system to define and control SSSI or the best examples of Scottish natural heritage of wildlife habitats, geological features and landforms. Also makes provisions for the protection of land from weeds such as Japanese Knotweed (see Weeds Act 1959). Lists species protected from disturbance, injury, intentional destruction or sale, eg nesting birds	Any activities that may impact upon birds, animals, plants or invasive plants should be undertaken in line within the guidance set out in this Act. The Act also provides for the notification of SSSIs and any works being undertaken on them	N/A	Planning During construction
Protection of Badgers Act 1992	The Act makes it an offence to: 1 Kill, injure or take a badger. 2 Cruelly ill-treat any badger. 3 Interfere with a badger sett.	If a site contains signs of badger activity an ecologist should be consulted to assess the site If known badger setts are within the site or will be disturbed by the activities of the site a license must be sought from SNH	N/A	Planning During construction
Weed Act 1959 (as amended)	Requires the occupiers of land on which injurious weeds are growing to take action to prevent the spread of such weeds. The Act specifies five such species: Common Ragwort, Spear thistle, Creeping Field thistle, Broad leaved dock and Curled dock	If injurious weeds are found on site guidance should be sought from Scottish Executive Environment and Rural Affairs Department	N/A	Planning During construction

Legislation	Key requirements	Direct site requirements	Indirect requirements	Application time planning/during construction/post
Northern Ireland				
Environmental Liability (Prevention and Remediation) Regulations (Northern Ireland) 2009	If any business activities cause environmental damage then it should be remedied. If there is a risk of damage from business activities, it must be prevented. The regulations do not apply to environmental damage caused before the regulations came into force. Overall, the Regulations are likely to be used only for the most serious cases of damage. Under the Regulations, environmental damage is: □ serious damage to surface or groundwater □ contamination of land where there is a significant risk to human health □ serious damage to EU protected natural habitats and species or damage to ASSIs	If any activities threaten to cause, or have caused, environmental damage then: □ take steps to prevent the damage (or further damage) occurring □ inform the NIEA or other authorities who will provide information on how to prevent and/or remedy the damage If the NIEA has to remedy the damage, then the company will have to pay the costs	N/A	Planning During construction Post construction

Legislation	Key requirements	Direct site requirements	Indirect requirements	Application time planning/during construction/post
Wildlife Order (Northern Ireland) 1985 (as amended)	Makes it an offence to intentionally kill, injure, or take any wild bird or their eggs or nests. The Order also prohibits certain methods of killing, injuring, or taking birds, restricts the sale and possession of captive bred birds, and sets standards for keeping birds in captivity. Similar rules apply to wild animals The Order makes it an offence to pick, uproot, trade in, or possess (for the purposes of trade) any wild plant listed in Schedule 8, and prohibits the unauthorised intentional uprooting of such plants The Order contains measures for preventing the establishment of species not native to Northern Ireland that may be detrimental to native wildlife	Any activities that may impact upon birds, animals, plants or invasive plants should be undertaken in line within the guidance set out in this Act. If in doubt guidance should be sought from the NIEA	N/A	Planning During construction
The Conservation (Natural Habitats) Regulations (Northern Ireland) 1995 (as amended)	The Department of the Environment (DoENI) designates SACs and SPAs in accordance with these Regulations. Under this legislation it is an offence to carry out any operation likely to damage a SAC or SPA without permission from the NIEA The maximum penalty for non-compliance is £5000 and an offender may be liable for the costs of restoring the damaged area to its original condition. Enforcement is by the Environment and Heritage Service (EHS)	Any activities undertaken that may affect a protected habitat listed under these Regulations should be discussed with the relevant NIEA before work starts	N/A	Planning During construction

Legislation	Key requirements	Direct site requirements	Indirect requirements	Application time planning/during construction/post
The Environment (Northern Ireland) Order 2002	The DOE designates ASSIs under this Order. The legislation makes it an offence to carry out operations likely to damage an ASSI without permission from the NIEA, DOE. It is also an offence to damage or destroy a protected scientific interest The maximum penalty for both offences is £20 000. In addition to a fine, offenders may be liable for the costs of restoring the damaged area to its original condition. Enforcement is by the Department of the Environment, Environment and Heritage Service	If any work is likely to impact upon an ASSI guidance should be sought from the NIEA before work starts	N/A	Planning During construction
Noxious Weeds (Northern Ireland) Order 1977	Requires the occupiers of land on which noxious weeds are growing to take action to prevent the spread of such weeds. The Act specifies such species as: Wild oat, Thistle, Dock and Ragwort (for further information contact Department of Agriculture and Rural Development (DARDNI))	If noxious weeds are found on site guidance should be sought from the Department of Agriculture and Rural Development	N/A	Planning During construction

4.3   Historic or ancient remains and built heritage

4.3.1   Why is it important to protect archaeological remains and built heritage?

Archaeological remains and built heritage are an irreplaceable and valuable part of our national heritage. Buildings and structures – some that are only a few decades old or others that are hundreds of years old – are important assets of the built environment and need preserving. For this reason both conservation and archaeological study of buried and built heritage are an important material consideration in the planning process.

Professional archaeologists may need to conduct on-site works to assess the nature and extent of any remains so that an archaeological statement can be submitted in support of a planning application. They may be commissioned as a condition of planning permission either to supervise their protection during construction works or to excavate and record remains that are to be destroyed. Archaeological and heritage considerations should be built early into the project plan to:

☐ ensure that remains to be preserved are protected by designing buildings and implementing construction processes that will not affect them

☐ prevent disruptions to project programmes and associated costs

☐ enable architects to add value by incorporating elements of the site's heritage in the final development

☐ comply with legal requirements relating to scheduled monuments, listed buildings and the protection of the historic environment generally through planning legislation.

The perception that archaeology will be found and construction will be stopped is widespread but frequently erroneous. Archaeological remains receive a range of designations and/or statutory protection. The most significant sites will be scheduled ancient monuments, however many are unscheduled but are still important. They are a material consideration in the planning process, as identified in various UK planning guidance notes. Archaeological evaluation may be required, for example, in support of a planning application, or excavation and standing building analysis as a condition of planning permission. Either way it needs to be planned and budgeted for long before costs and programmes are finalised and an application is lodged, or opportunities will be missed and unexpected costs and delays may then arise.

A scheduled monuments consent from the Secretary of State is required before any works to or around a scheduled monument can take place. Also, consent is required for any works affecting the setting of the monument (ie works taking place outside the scheduled area). Carrying out unauthorised works is a criminal offence that incurs significant penalties.

This section covers the source of archaeological information, managing remains on site, protection of features, removal of human remains, treasure trove and protected buildings.

4.3.2 Sources of archaeological information

Depending on the project's nature and location, work may have been undertaken to investigate the archaeological, architectural or historical significance of the site during the planning stage. Examples of this work are outlined here because it may be a useful source of information about the site. Generally it is the client's responsibility to ensure that sufficient investigation has been undertaken to satisfy planning requirements (these are identified in local and national planning policies. See the Further guidance box at the end of this section). However, this responsibility can transfer to the contractor in a design and build scheme.

Where important archaeological remains (whether they are scheduled or not) are affected by a proposed development, the emphasis is on preserving them. If preservation in situ is not feasible, an archaeological excavation or building analysis for the purposes of understanding and public dissemination may be an acceptable alternative.

When applying for planning permission, clients may be advised by the local planning authority to commission a desk-based archaeological assessment report as supporting documentation to the planning application. This report will review the archaeological potential of the site, assess the impact of the proposed scheme and propose a mitigation strategy.

If there is not enough information to decide how to proceed with the site, an evaluation may be proposed, which may involve the following:

Phase I survey: a desk based review of the site using available archaeological resources, eg tithe maps, Chapman and Andre maps, old RAF aerial photography and online databases.

Phase II survey: archaeological field evaluation that may include non-intrusive geophysical surveys and aerial photography or intrusive investigation by boreholes/auguring and trial pits/trenches (see Figure 4.10). It may be possible to save time and money by combining aspects of this work with geotechnical investigation

Using all available information, including the results of any assessment and/or evaluation, the local planning authority will decide how the archaeological issues on that site should be managed: it may refuse or grant permission without condition, or it may impose a planning obligation or condition on planning permission. It may issue a brief setting out what works are to be undertaken and then require a written scheme of investigation to be submitted for approval before works begin.

Figure 4.10
A 19th century pottery kiln found on a brownfield site (courtesy MoLAS)

As archaeological evaluations and excavations usually occur early in the project they may be specified in the contract, particularly where the contractor is to provide attendances for the archaeological work.

Consideration should be given to the season in which archaeological works are undertaken, so that they can be carried out at the most opportune time.

4.3.3   Managing archaeological remains on site

If it is likely that archaeological or historical features will be found during a project, the client will probably have commissioned some work on the site. Contact the client for any information they hold about the site.

Even if an investigation has been carried out there may be a potential for unexpected finds to be uncovered, particularly during earthworks and excavation (see Section 3.3). The contractor's responsibilities and liabilities will depend on the contract type and the site manager should be aware of the requirements.

Depending on the contract, the discovery of ancient structures and deposits on site could lead to secondary impacts, such as the necessity to stockpile large quantities of material (see Section 4.5.5) while further investigation is being carried out, the generation of dust (see Section 4.1.2) or effects on site ecology (see Section 4.2.2).

It will be necessary to comply with any contract and planning conditions and obligations (ie any conditions that may be attached to the planning permission).

4.3.4   Protection of known archaeological or historical features

Ensure that the proposed method of working complies with any obligations identified. Works that are located close to a site of archaeological or cultural significance can have a damaging effect. For example, vibration or tunnelling could cause cracking and subsidence in listed buildings. Access road traffic could disturb sensitive historic structures.

The levels of vibration that can cause damage to buildings vary considerably. It is always worth agreeing with the client the condition of susceptible buildings/monuments before works begin, and monitoring them after. Seek specialist advice if vibration is likely to be a problem (see Section 4.6.7). Highlight the potential for significant effects on such buildings/ monuments to site staff and identify control measures before starting work.

Dewatering works can cause draw-down of water and differential settlement, affecting archaeological materials that had been well preserved by being waterlogged. In such cases ensure that there is agreement on how to avoid or minimise such damage.

Case study 4.2
Inappropriate management of a scheduled
monument (courtesy MoLAS)

In the late 1980s construction of an office development was underway at Cannon Street Station, London, a site known to overlie important Roman buildings and waterfront designated as a scheduled monument. Only limited below ground works were proposed and these were given scheduled monument consent, subject to an intervention by the Museum of London. In the course of development further drainage works were necessary, including a deep inspection chamber, which was constructed without a revised consent application for archaeological intervention.

The principle contractor was prosecuted for causing works to be executed damaging a scheduled monument, found guilty and fined £1000 with £20 000 costs.

4.3.5   Heritage and professional bodies

The heritage bodies have a general duty to conserve heritage, schedule and undertake research etc. Unless dealing with scheduled ancient monuments, contact the local planning authority archaeologist in the first instance for archaeological matters and the local authority conservation officer for listed buildings. The county/local authority/regional and island archaeologist has responsibility for planning issues.

Heritage body	Contact details
Cadw (Welsh Historic Monuments)	Tel: 01443 336 000
English Heritage	Tel: 0870 333 1181
Historic Scotland	Tel: 0131 668 8600
Northern Ireland Environment Agency	Tel: 0845 302 0008

The professional institutes assess and regulate historic environment professionals, and publish guidance on heritage good practice. The Institute for Archaeologists has a registered organisations scheme that quality assured historic environment practices belong to.

Professional body	Contact details
Institute for Archaeologists (lists Registered Archaeological Organisations, the QA scheme for archaeology)	Tel: 0118 378 6446 <www.archaeologists.net>
Institute of Historic Building Conservation	Tel: 01747 873 133 <www.ihbc.org.uk>

4.3.6   Removal of human remains

The law concerning the disturbance of buried human remains varies across the UK. The requirements regarding whether or not permission is required and the terms of any conditions and licences are complex, so advice from an accredited archaeologist is important if it is likely that burials will be encountered, or if human remains are found unexpectedly.

Figure 4.11
The unexpected discovery of human remains can cause delays (courtesy MoLAS)

Local authorities are responsible for protecting a wide range of archaeological remains. Where development threatens to damage or destroy remains, the authority can require appropriate investigation through a planning condition or legal agreement. In certain circumstances it can also secure the positive long-term management of sites.

4.3.7   Treasure trove

Under the Treasure Act 1996 (for England, Wales and Northern Ireland), certain finds are treasure, including:

1   Coins that are at least 300 years old.

2   Objects containing at least 10 per cent of gold or silver and at least 300 years old.

3   Any object that is found near to known treasure.

It is the obligation of the finder to report to the coroner for the district in which the treasure was found.

4.3.8   Protected buildings

Listed buildings

In giving a building statutory protection against unauthorised demolition, alteration and extension, listing is an integral part of the system for managing change to the environment through the planning process administered by local planning authorities and the relevant government department.

Planning authorities and national park authorities have the power to serve a building preservation notice (BPN) on the owner of a building that is not listed, but which they consider is of special architectural or historic interest and is in danger of demolition or alteration in such a way as to affect its character.

A BPN provides protection to a building. For a period of six months after service of the BPN it is subject to the same rules as if it were listed, which allows time for a formal assessment to be carried out.

Generally the planning authority serves a BPN on the owner of the building and then requests that the building be considered for listing. The Secretary of State must decide within six months whether to list the building. If it is not listed, compensation may be payable if loss has been sustained because of the BPN.

Buildings of special architectural or historic interest

Ministers are responsible for compiling the statutory list of buildings of special architectural or historic interest. The heritage body is responsible for providing expert advice that buildings meet the criteria for listing, and for administering the process.

The heritage body is responsible for considering and advising on all applications for listing, and for making recommendations to the Secretary of State about whether to add buildings to the statutory list, based on set criteria. Before a full assessment is made, the owner and local authority will be informed that listing is being considered (unless the building is considered to be under immediate threat), and asked for comments.

If there is any doubt about the significance of the building, the heritage body may undertake historical and documentary research, and make comparisons with other examples of the same building type. In most cases an inspection will be undertaken, although this is not always necessary. Where the heritage body considers that an inspection is desirable, the owner's permission will be sought.

When the assessment is complete, and any comments from the owner and local authority considered, the recommendation will be sent to the relevant minister. Once a decision has been reached, the owner, applicant and local authority will be notified, and sent a letter detailing the reasons for the decision.

The starting point for finding out information about the heritage implications of any area of land should be the local planning authority's historic environment record.

It should be noted that six weeks "operations notice" to the planning authority is required for any proposals to disturb the ground, tip on it or flood it.

4.3.9 Good practice checklists

Watching brief

Be prepared for unexpected finds whether or not known archaeological or historical features have been identified on site	
During excavations look out for burned or blackened material, brick or tile fragments, coins, pottery or bone fragments, skeletons, timber joists or post holes, brick or stone foundations, in-filled ditches	
If addressed at the right time and in the right way, finds may not affect the progress of the works	
If unsure about a find call in an archaeologist to assess it	
An archaeologist employed by the company may be able to agree suitable mitigation strategies with the planning authority archaeologist	
With the right advice delays may be much less than any statutory period	
If any unexpected finds are encountered	
Immediately stop work in the area	
Protect the find by fencing/blocking it off and contact the site manager	
Contact the local archaeological officer at the local authority	
Consider seeking specialist archaeological advice on how to proceed	
If human remains are discovered a licence may be required before works can continue: an archaeologist can advise	
Contractor responsibilities (though not expected to be an expert)	
Pursue the contractual obligations, eg providing attendances and/or access to professional archaeologists, sharing of health and safety documentation	
Protect known archaeological and heritage sites	
Report any significant finds arising during construction	

4.3.10 Further guidance

BARBER B, CARVER, J, HINTON, P and NIXON, T (2008) *Archaeology and development. A good practice guide to managing risk and maximising benefit*, C672, CIRIA, London (ISBN: 978-0-86017-672-5)

DAVIS, M J, GDANIEC, K L A, BRICE, M and WHITE, L (2004) *Mitigation of construction impacts on archaeological remains*, Museum of London Archaeology Service, annotated edition (ISBN: 978-1901992472)

ENGLISH HERITAGE (2002) *Environmental archaeology. A guide to the theory and practice of methods, from sampling and recovery to post-excavation*, Centre for Archaeology Guidelines, English Heritage, London *

FIDLER, J, WOOD, C AND RIDOUT, B (2004) *Flooding and historic buildings*, Technical Advice Note, English Heritage, London *

HISTORIC SCOTLAND (2010) *Managing change in the historic environment – guidance notes*, Historic Scotland, Edinburgh. Go to: <www.historic-scotland.gov.uk/index/heritage/policy/managingchange.htm>

ISC (2004) *ICE conditions of contract for archaeological investigation*, first edition, Institution of Civil Engineers, UK (ISBN: 978-0-7277-3237-8)

Statutes

DCMS (2007) Treasure Act 1996 Code of Practice (2nd Revision) England and Wales, Department for Culture, Media and Sport, London *

Planning Advice Note 42 *Archaeology – the planning process and scheduled monument procedures,* The Scottish Government, Edinburgh (ISBN: 0-74800-833-0) *

Planning Policy Guidance 16 (1990): *Archaeology and planning for England*, Communities and Local Government, London (ISBN: 978-0-11752-353-1) *

Planning Policy Statement (PPS) 9 (2005) *Biodiversity and geological conservation*, Communities and Local Government, London (ISBN: 978-0-11753-954-9) *

Planning Policy Statement (PPS) 5 (2010) *Planning for the historic environment*, Communities and Local Government, London (ISBN: 978-0-11754-095-8) *

Scottish Planning Policy 2010: *A statement of the Scottish Government's policy on nationally important land use planning matters*, The Scottish Government, Edinburgh *

Welsh Office Circular 60-96: *Planning and the historic environment – archaeology*, Welsh Assembly Government, Cardiff (ISBN: 1-85760-092-4) *

Welsh Office Circular 61-96: *Planning and the historic environment –
historic buildings and conservation areas*, Welsh Assembly Government,
Cardiff *

* denotes that a copy of the document is included on the
accompanying resource CD

Relevant toolbox talks
(refer to Appendix A4)

Archaeology

4.3.11 Legislation

The following table is a brief summary of applicable legislation for historic
or ancient remains and built heritage, including requirements and divided
by UK region. Due to frequent legislative developments users should check
<**www.netregs.gov.uk**> when using the table.

Legislation	Key requirements	Direct site requirements	Indirect requirements	Application time planning/during construction/post
England				
Ancient Monuments and Archaeological Areas Act 1979	Scheduled monument consent is required for any works involving "demolishing, destroying, removing, repairing, altering, adding to, flooding or tipping material onto the monument or around it"	If any scheduled monument is present on site a scheduled monument consent must be sought from the Department of Culture Media and Sport (DCMS)	N/A	Planning During construction
The Planning (Listed Buildings and Conservation Areas) Act 1990	Any works involving the demolition, alteration, or extension, of a listed building that would affect its character as a listed building requires consent from English Heritage Local authorities can designate as conservation areas any area of special architectural or historic interest, the character or appearance of which is desirable to preserve or enhance. Most authorities will provide supplementary planning guidance for such areas	If a listed building will be affected by the works a consent must be obtained from English Heritage If the site is listed as a conservation area advice should be sought from the local authority as to any supplementary planning guidance	N/A	Planning During construction

Legislation	Key requirements	Direct site requirements	Indirect requirements	Application time planning/during construction/post
England				
Burials Act 1857 & Disused Burial Grounds Act 1981	Under the Burials Act 1857 it is necessary to obtain a license from the Home Office to disturb any burials The Disused Burial Grounds Act 1981 sets stringent conditions regarding the removal and disposal of human remains	If any human remains are anticipated/found on site a license must be sought to disturb the remains If there is any likelihood that human remains may be encountered during construction specialist archaeological advice should be sought on obtaining proper legal authority to disturb them	N/A	Planning During construction
Wales				
Ancient Monuments and Archaeological Areas Act 1979	Scheduled monument consent is required for any works involving "demolishing, destroying, removing, repairing, altering, adding to, flooding or tipping material onto the monument or around it"	If any scheduled monument is present on site a scheduled monument consent must be sought from Cadw	N/A	Planning During construction

Legislation	Key requirements	Direct site requirements	Indirect requirements	Application time planning/during construction/post
The Planning (Listed Buildings and Conservation Areas) Act 1990	Any works involving the demolition, alteration, or extension, of a listed building that would affect its character as a listed building requires consent from Cadw Local authorities can designate as conservation areas any area of special architectural or historic interest, the character or appearance of which is desirable to preserve or enhance. Most authorities will provide supplementary planning guidance for such areas	If a listed building will be affected by the works a consent must be obtained from Cadw If the site is listed as a conservation area advice should be sought from the Local authority as to any supplementary planning guidance	N/A	Planning During construction
Burials Act 1857 & Disused Burial Grounds Act 1981	Under the Burials Act 1857 it is necessary to obtain a license to disturb any burials The Disused Burial Grounds Act 1981 sets stringent conditions regarding the removal and disposal of human remains	If any human remains are anticipated/found on site a license must be sought to disturb the remains If there is any likelihood that human remains may be encountered during construction specialist archaeological advice should be sought on obtaining proper legal authority to disturb them	N/A	Planning During construction

Legislation	Key requirements	Direct site requirements	Indirect requirements	Application time planning/during construction/post
Scotland				
Ancient Monuments and Archaeological Areas Act 1979	Scheduled monument consent is required for any works involving "demolishing, destroying, removing, repairing, altering, adding to, flooding or tipping material onto the monument"	If any scheduled monument is present on site a scheduled monument consent must be sought from Historic Scotland	N/A	Planning During construction
The Planning (Listed Buildings and Conservation Areas) Act 1997	Any works involving the demolition, alteration, or extension, of a listed building that would affect its character as a listed building require consent from Historic Scotland. Local authorities can also designate as conservation areas any area of special architectural or historic interest, the character or appearance of which is desirable to preserve or enhance. Most local authorities will provide supplementary planning guidance for such areas	If a listed building will be affected by the works a consent must be obtained from Historic Scotland If the site is listed as a conservation area advice should be sought from the Local authority as to any supplementary planning guidance	N/A	Planning During construction

Legislation	Key requirements	Direct site requirements	Indirect requirements	Application time planning/during construction/post
Removal of Human Remains	Unlike England there is no faculty or license system specific to human remains	It is normal practice to check with the procurator fiscal that no offence would be committed under laws relating to public decency or the violation of sepulchres provisions, and a warrant may be sought from Historic Scotland to this effect. If there is any likelihood that human remains may be encountered during construction specialist archaeological advice should be sought on obtaining proper permission to disturb them	N/A	Planning During construction
Northern Ireland				
Ancient Monuments and Archaeological Areas Act 1979	Scheduled monument consent is required for any works involving "demolishing, destroying, removing, repairing, altering, adding to, flooding or tipping material onto the monument"	If any scheduled monument is present on site a scheduled monument consent must be sought from the NIEA	N/A	Planning During construction

Legislation	Key requirements	Direct site requirements	Indirect requirements	Application time planning/during construction/post
The Planning (Listed Buildings and Conservation Areas) Act 1990	Any works involving the demolition, alteration, or extension, of a listed building that would affect its character as a listed building requires consent from NIEA The Department of the Environment Northern Ireland (DOENI) can designate as conservation areas any area of special architectural or historic interest, the character or appearance of which is desirable to preserve or enhance. The DOENI will provide supplementary planning guidance for such areas	If a listed building will be affected by the works a consent must be obtained from the NIEA If the site is listed as a conservation area advice should be sought from the DOENI as to any supplementary planning guidance	N/A	Planning During construction
Burials Act 1857 & Disused Burial Grounds Act 1981	Under the Burials Act 1857 it is necessary to obtain a license to disturb any burials The Disused Burial Grounds Act 1981 sets stringent conditions regarding the removal and disposal of human remains	If any human remains are anticipated/found on site a license must be sought to disturb the remains If there is any likelihood that human remains may be encountered during construction specialist archaeological advice should be sought on obtaining proper legal authority to disturb them	N/A	Planning During construction

4.4   Land contamination

4.4.1   Why is managing contaminated land important?

Contaminated land often occurs because of previous land use, for example industrial processes or landfill.

Land contamination may present a risk to the users of the land, to ecological systems, to buildings, and to surface and groundwaters. Exposure to contamination can be through inhalation of dust or gases, contact with soil or via food grown on the land. Leachates (dissolved contaminant liquid) can pollute ground and surface water.

If contamination is likely to be encountered the contract should define the methods for dealing with it. The contract should refer to the guidance issued by the statutory authorities on how to manage contamination.

Contaminated land may result in the following problems:

☐ delays to the programme through unexpected or accidental contamination

☐ liability for costs of making contamination worse because of activities on site or for the management and/or remediation of contamination

☐ pollution of groundwater and surface watercourses

☐ pollution of surrounding land

☐ effects on flora or fauna

☐ public concern and anxiety.

This section advises on how to deal with contamination (both expected and unexpected), how to avoid causing or spreading contamination and procedures to manage the discovery of unexploded ordnance.

4.4.2   The source-pathway-receptor model

An important consideration when dealing with contamination on site is the relationship between the source of the contaminant (eg a leak from an underground oil storage tank), the pathway along which the contaminant can migrate beyond the site (including groundwater) and the receptor (eg the aquifer). This is the basis of the source-pathway-receptor model (pollutant linkage) as illustrated Figure 4.12.

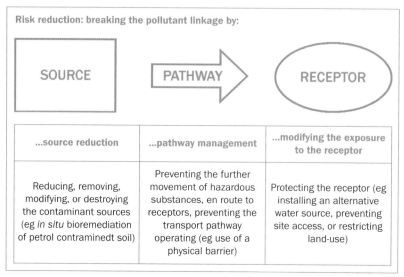

Figure 4.12   *Source-pathway-receptor model*

Contamination identified on site does not necessarily pose a threat on site or to potential receptors in areas surrounding the site if it is left undisturbed, but work activities can mobilise contaminants (eg excavation puncturing a protective barrier). This can cause a pollution incident away from the site. The site manager and/or contractor is then liable for the contamination.

4.4.3   How to avoid problems

Many problems associated with the discovery of contamination on site can be successfully managed. However, if they are not managed, they can cause problems by spreading the contaminants across or off the site. Activities that can lead to this occurring include:

☐   wind-blown contaminated dust arising from loading of lorries

☐   stockpiling contaminated material on clean ground during works

☐   spillages of contaminants such as oil or chemicals onto the ground during works

☐   dewatering of excavations that draws in contaminated groundwater from nearby sites

☐   potential for release of volatile vapours

☐   discharge of contaminated water into nearby watercourses (eg by site dewatering).

Responsibilities

It is the responsibility of the client to conduct good quality site investigations to determine the potential for contamination on site. Often this will be subcontracted by the client to a suitably-qualified and experienced consultant, however overall responsibility still resides with the client. The process should follow that set out in the Contaminated Land Report (CLR) 11 model procedures framework. CLR 11 identifies several phases of site investigation and risk assessment to ensure that the site is suitable for use and provides guidance on the development of a remediation strategy that should be agreed by the planning authority and the regulator before any work begins. This should be done by the consultant and client.

Contractors have a duty to ensure they are given all the background information regarding the site and that they understand the history of the site and the actions they have to take to fulfil the requirements of the remediation strategy.

The remediation strategy to deal with contamination found on site should be derived from a tiered risk assessment approach in accordance with CLR 11, which includes the following stages of data gathering:

Preliminary investigation (Phase 1)

Phase 1 is mainly a desk-based exercise and "walkover", to identify whether there are any potentially contaminative sources present, this data includes:

☐   history of the site (details of its owners, occupiers and users)

☐   details of processes previously used on site (including their locations, raw materials, products, waste residues and methods of disposal)

☐   layout of the site above and below ground at each stage of development (including roadways, storage areas and other hard cover areas)

☐   presence of waste disposal areas, made ground, abandoned pits and quarries

☐   mining history (including shafts and roadways)

☐ information on geology and hydrogeology (including the presence of groundwater and surface water)

☐ other sources of potential contamination, such as current or historical uses of adjacent land.

Figure 4.13
Soil testing being
undertaken (courtesy
Parsons Brinckerhoff)

Site characterisation (Phase 2)

If the preliminary investigation finds that there are potentially unacceptable risks, more or less detailed, exploratory investigations would need to be undertaken by the client until it is possible to define:

☐ the type

☐ the concentration of contaminants

☐ the location and extent of any contamination on the site

☐ whether it does amount to "contamination" requiring remediation.

Initially an intrusive site investigation will be carried out using generic assessment criteria. If this identifies the presence of contamination a further detailed quantitative risk assessment (DQRA) will be carried out.

Although a robust site characterisation reduces the likelihood of discovering contamination during site works, unearthing unknown sources of contamination is always possible. Method statements should always include the possibility of finding contamination and the mechanisms for dealing with it. Site personnel (especially excavator operators and drilling contractors) should be vigilant during excavations (see visual signs checklist at the end of the section).

4.4.4   What to do if unexpected contamination is encountered

The contractor should already have adopted appropriate working methods to deal with contamination that is unexpected. These will be detailed in the remediation implementation plan (see Section 4.4.3).

During boring, digging, excavating and similar operations, the relevant operators should observe the uncovered ground and watch out for visual signs of contamination. Also, the release of noxious fumes, petrol, oils, solvents, chemical residues and smells may indicate contamination.

When contamination is suspected:

1   Stop work immediately.

2   Report the discovery to the site manager who must seek expert advice.

3   Seal off the area and contain any spread of contaminants.

4   Clear the affected area of the site to ensure there is nothing that could cause a fire or explosion.

5   Contact the regulator usually the local authority if it suspected or likely that contamination has been found.

6   Ensure that the suspected contamination is tested and characterised and agree changes to any existing remedial plan or produce a remedial plan if none exists.

7   Follow good practice guidance to remediate the land.

Testing and analysis

Testing and analysis should be carried out on spoil and other materials if there is any doubt that these materials are contaminated. Sampling should be carried out in accordance with good practice by competent specialists. Samples taken should be sent to a competent laboratory for testing against a suite of contaminants. The method of sampling and the scoping of the testing should be determined by the site, as defined by a competent person (eg consultant).

Chemical testing of soils carried out using the Monitoring Certification Scheme (MCerts) performance standard provides assurances on the reliability of data from such tests. The performance standard is an application of ISO 17025:2000 specifically for the chemical testing of soil and covers:

☐   the selection and validation of methods

☐   sampling pre-treatment and preparation

☐   the estimation of measurement uncertainty

☐   participation in proficiency testing schemes

☐   the reporting of results and information.

The results of the testing will determine whether the materials are contaminated and/or hazardous and whether they require appropriate disposal. Alternatively, if the materials are uncontaminated they may be reused on the site of production or sent to an exempt waste management site.

Figure 4.14
Remediation (courtesy
Parsons Brinckerhoff)

4.4.5   Remediating contaminated land (Phase 3)

If the intrusive site investigation identifies that contamination exists, a
remediation action plan will be produced, for example by the client's
consultant, identifying suitable remediation. There are various options
available for dealing with contaminated land once it has been identified on
site. The majority of remedial techniques to be carried out on site require
an appropriate environmental permit or exemption. Remediation options
can be divided into:

Containment

☐   excavation and disposal of the contaminated material, however
    disposal to landfill is not generally encouraged

☐   physically through covers, barriers or liners, or chemical stabilisation.

Separation

☐   physical separation of contaminants from the rest of the soil through
    soil washing, solvent extraction or particle separation.

Destruction

☐   physically through incineration

☐   chemically through, eg chlorination

☐   biologically through the introduction of micro-organisms into the soil or through phytoremediation (use of plants).

These options should be considered on a site-by-site basis and the best practicable technique will be stipulated in the remediation strategy. These options can be divided into many techniques, summarised in Figure 4.15.

4.4.6   Unexploded ordnance

The discovery of unexploded ordnance on site is unusual, and is only likely to occur in areas of historic weapons manufacture or storage during the world wars. However, they may be discovered in areas that received heavy bombardment during the Second World War such as London, Liverpool and Coventry. If unexploded ordnance is suspected or found on site:

☐   stop work immediately

☐   clear and secure the area

☐   contact the police.

> If there is any doubt about the condition of the ground on which the development is to take place, stop work and get the advice of a suitably qualified person.

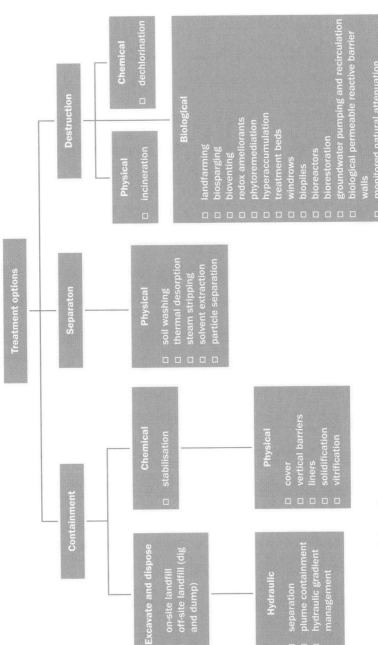

Figure 4.15 Remediation options

4.4.7   Good practice checklists

Getting to know the site and remedial plans

Carry out a preliminary investigation of site using the approach set out in CLR 11	
If indicated, undertake exploratory investigations of the site to characterise contamination on site in terms of: ☐ type ☐ concentration ☐ extent and location	
Develop a remediation strategy from the results of preliminary and exploratory investigations	
Agree the remediation strategy with the local planning authority and make it available to the contractor	
Ensure relevant permits are in place for any remedial works required	

Avoid causing or spreading contamination

Do not stockpile contaminated soil unless it cannot be avoided. If it is necessary, stockpile only on a hardstanding area to prevent contamination of underlying ground	
Cover stockpiled material to prevent wind-blown dust (potentially contaminated) and to prevent ingress of rainwater	
Control surface drainage from stockpiled area. Water draining from a stockpile may be contaminated and need controlled off-site disposal	
Take care when handling, storing and using oils and chemicals	

Visual signs of contamination

Discoloured soil (eg chemical residues)	
Unexpected odours (eg hydrocarbons such as petrol)	
Fibrous texture to the soil (eg asbestos)	
Presence of foreign objects (eg chemical/oil containers/waste)	

Presence of foreign objects (eg chemical/oil containers/waste)	
Evidence of previous soil workings	
Evidence of underground structures and tanks	
Existence of waste pits	
Artificial ground where the level has been raised by man's activities and not due to a natural cause, eg slag heaps	
Old drain runs and contamination within buildings such as tanks, flues etc	
Topsoil near to motorways can be contaminated by particulate deposition	

4.4.8   Further guidance

Regulatory

CLG (2004) Planning Policy Statement (PPS) 23 *Planning and pollution control*, Communities and Local Government, London (ISBN: 978-0-117539-279-3) *

CLG (2004) Planning Policy Statement (PPS) 23: *Planning and pollution control: Annex 2 – development on land affected by contamination*, Communities and Local Government, London (ISBN: 978-0-11753-927-3) *

DEFRA and ENVIRONMENT AGENCY (2004) *Model procedures for the management of land contamination*, CLR11, Environment Agency, Bristol (ISBN: 1-84432-295-5) *

ENVIRONMENT AGENCY (2004) *Framework for the classification of contaminated soil as hazardous waste*, version 1, Environment Agency, Bristol *

ENVIRONMENT AGENCY (2004) *Decommissioning redundant boreholes and wells*, SCHO0499BEHE-e-e, Environment Agency, Bristol *

ENVIRONMENT AGENCY, SCOTTISH ENVIRONMENT PROTECTION AGENCY, ENVIRONMENT AND HERITAGE SERVICE (2008) *Technical Guidance WM2: Hazardous waste: interpretation of the definition and classification of hazardous waste*, second edition, version 2.2 Environment Agency, Bristol (ISBN: 1 84432 454 0) *

HSE (1991) *Protection of workers and the general public during the development of contaminated land*, HSG66, Health and Safety Executive, Bootle (ISBN: 0-11885-657-X)

Further guidance and documentation can be found at <www.environment-agency.gov.uk/research/planning/33706.aspx>

General guidance

BAKER, K, HAYWARD, H, POTTER, L *et al* (2009) *The VOCs Handbook. Investigating, assessing and managing risks from inhalation of VOCs at land affected by contamination*, C682, CIRIA, London (ISBN: 978-0-86017-685-5)

CL:AIRE (2008) *The definition of waste: development of industry code of practicce*, Contaminated Land: Applications in Real Environments (CL:AIRE), London

RUDLAND, D J and JACKSON, S D (2004) *Selection of remedial treatments for contaminated land. A guide to good practice*, C622, CIRIA, London (ISBN: 978-0-86017-622-0)

RUDLAND, D J, LANCEFIELD, R M and MAYELL, P N (2001) *Contaminated land risk assessment. A guide to good practice*, C552, CIRIA, London (ISBN: 978-0-86017-552-0)

STEEDS, J E, SHEPHERD, E andBARRY, D L (1996) *A guide for safe working on contaminated sites*, R132, CIRIA, London (ISBN: 978-0-86017-451-6)

STONE, K, MURRAY, A, COOKE, S and FORAN, J(2009) *Unexploded ordnance (UXO) A guide for the construction industry*, C681, CIRIA, London (ISBN: 978-0-86017-681-7)

WILSON, S, OLIVER, S, MALLETT, H, HUTCHINGS, H and CARD, G (2007) *Assessing risks posed by hazardous ground gases to buildings*, C665, CIRIA, London (ISBN: 978-0-86017-665-7)

Statutues

BS BS 10175:2001: *Investigation of potentially contaminated sites – code of practice*

*   denotes that a copy of the document is included on the accompanying resource CD

Relevant toolbox talks (refer to Appendix A4)
Spill control
Storage of waste
Oil/diesel storage
Archaeology
Bentonite
Washing down plant and machinery
Working on previously developed land.

4.4.9   Legislation

The following table is a brief summary of applicable legislation to land contamination, including requirements and divided by UK region. Due to frequent legislative developments users should check <**www.netregs.gov.uk**> when using the table.

Legislation	Key requirements	Direct site requirements	Indirect requirements	Application time planning/during construction/post
England				
The Environmental Damage (Prevention and Remediation) Regulations 2009	If a business carries out an activity that causes environmental damage they will have to remedy the damage. If there is a risk of damage from any business activities, the damage must be prevented The regulations do not apply to environmental damage caused before the regulations came into force Overall, the regulations are likely to be used only for the most serious cases of damage Under the regulations, environmental damage is: ☐ serious damage to surface or groundwater ☐ contamination of land where there is a significant risk to human health ☐ serious damage to EU protected natural habitats and species or damage to SSSIs	If any activities threaten to cause, or have caused, environmental damage then: ☐ take steps to prevent the damage (or further damage) occurring ☐ inform the Environment Agency or other authorities who will provide information on how to prevent and/or remedy the damage If the Environment Agency or another authority has to remedy the damage then the company will be liable to pay the costs	N/A	Planning During construction Post construction

Legislation	Key requirements	Direct site requirements	Indirect requirements	Application time planning/during construction/post
Environmental Protection Act 1990 (as amended) (Part 2A)	It requires that local authorities identify contaminated land and ensure that significant risks are dealt with. It also establishes rules for who should pay for remediation (in conjunction with the Environmental Damage (Prevention and Remediation) Regulations 2009)	If any contaminated land is discovered on site or contamination caused while on site, immediate consultation should be sought with the local authority	N/A	Planning During construction Post construction
Contaminated Land (England) Regulations 2006	Further define land contamination and special sites also explains the rules for how appeals can be made against decisions taken under the Part 2A regime	If any contaminated land is discovered on site or contamination caused while on site, immediate consultation should be sought with the local authority	N/A	Planning During construction Post construction
Town and Country Planning Act 1990	Under this Act local planning authorities are responsible for ensuring that land contamination is dealt with through the planning system and that remediation takes place where it is required It is the responsibility of the developer to carry out the remediation and satisfy the local authority that the remediation has been carried out as agreed	Before undertaking works where contaminated land is present or if contaminated land is discovered on site during construction, advice should be sought from the local authority before continuing work	N/A	Planning During construction Post construction

Legislation	Key requirements	Direct site requirements	Indirect requirements	Application time planning/during construction/post
Wales				
Environmental Damage (Prevention and Remediation) (Wales) Regulations 2009	If any business activities cause environmental damage then it should be remedied. If there is a risk of damage from business activities then it must be prevented The regulations do not apply to environmental damage caused before the regulations came into force Overall, the regulations are likely to be used only for the most serious cases of damage Under the regulations, environmental damage is: ☐ serious damage to surface or groundwater ☐ contamination of land where there is a significant risk to human health ☐ serious damage to EU protected natural habitats and species or damage to SSSIs	If any activities threaten to cause, or have caused, environmental damage then: ☐ take steps to prevent the damage (or further damage) occurring ☐ inform the Environment Agency or other authorities who will provide information on how to prevent and/or remedy the damage If the Environment Agency or another authority has to remedy the damage then the company will be liable to pay the costs	N/A	Planning During construction Post construction

Legislation	Key requirements	Direct site requirements	Indirect requirements	Application time planning/during construction/post
Environmental Protection Act 1990 (as amended) (Part 2A)	It requires that local authorities identify contaminated land and ensure that significant risks are dealt with. It also establishes rules for who should pay for remediation (in conjunction with the Environmental Damage (Prevention and Remediation) Regulations 2009)	If any contaminated land is discovered on site or contamination caused while on site, immediate consultation should be sought with the local authority	N/A	Planning During construction Post construction
Contaminated Land (Wales) Regulations 2006	Further define land contamination and special sites also explains the rules for how appeals can be made against decisions taken under the Part 2A regime	If any contaminated land is discovered on site or contamination caused while on site, immediate consultation should be sought with the local authority	N/A	Planning During construction Post construction
Town and Country Planning Act 1990	Under this Act local planning authorities are responsible for ensuring that land contamination is dealt with through the planning system and that remediation takes place where it is required It is the responsibility of the developer to carry out the remediation and satisfy the local authority that the remediation has been carried out as agreed	Before undertaking works where contaminated land is present or if contaminated land is discovered on site during construction, advice should be sought from the local authority before continuing work	N/A	Planning During construction Post construction

Legislation	Key requirements	Direct site requirements	Indirect requirements	Application time planning/during construction/post
Scotland				
Environmental Liability (Scotland) Regulations 2009 SSI 266	If any business activities cause environmental damage then it should be remedied. If there is a risk of damage from business activities then it must be prevented The regulations do not apply to environmental damage caused before the regulations came into force Overall, the regulations are likely to be used only for the most serious cases of damage Under the regulations, environmental damage is: ☐ serious damage to surface or groundwater ☐ contamination of land where there is a significant risk to human health ☐ serious damage to EU protected natural habitats and species or damage to SSSIs	If any activities threaten to cause, or have caused, environmental damage then: ☐ take steps to prevent the damage (or further damage) occurring ☐ inform SEPA or other authorities who will provide information on how to prevent and/or remedy the damage If SEPA has to remedy the damage then the company will be liable to pay the costs	N/A	Planning During construction Post construction

Legislation	Key requirements	Direct site requirements	Indirect requirements	Application time planning/during construction/post
Environmental Protection Act 1990 (as amended) (Part 2A)	It requires that local authorities identify contaminated land and ensure that significant risks are dealt with. It also establishes rules for who should pay for remediation (in conjunction with the Environmental Damage (Prevention and Remediation) Regulations 2009). See Planning Advice Note 33 for further guidance	If any contaminated land is discovered on site or contamination caused while on site, immediate consultation should be sought with SEPA	N/A	Planning During construction Post construction
Contaminated Land (Scotland) Regulations 2000 as amended by 2005 regulations	Further define land contamination and special sites also explains the rules for how appeals can be made against decisions taken under the Part 2A regime	If any contaminated land is discovered on site or contamination caused while on site, immediate consultation should be sought with SEPA	N/A	Planning During construction Post construction

Legislation	Key requirements	Direct site requirements	Indirect requirements	Application time *planning/during construction/post*
Northern Ireland				
Environmental Liability (Prevention and Remediation) Regulations (Northern Ireland) 2009	If any business activities cause environmental damage then it should be remedied. If there is a risk of damage from business activities then it must be prevented The regulations do not apply to environmental damage caused before the regulations came into force Overall, the regulations are likely to be used only for the most serious cases of damage Under the regulations, environmental damage is: ☐ serious damage to surface or groundwater ☐ contamination of land where there is a significant risk to human health ☐ serious damage to EU protected natural habitats and species or damage to ASSIs	If any activities threaten to cause, or have caused, environmental damage then: ☐ take steps to prevent the damage (or further damage) occurring ☐ inform the NIEA or other authorities who will provide information on how to prevent and/or remedy the damage If the NIEA has to remedy the damage then the company will be liable to pay the costs	N/A	Planning During construction Post construction

Legislation	Key requirements	Direct site requirements	Indirect requirements	Application time planning/*during* *construction/post*
Waste and Contaminated Land (Northern Ireland) Order 1997	Sets out the waste management regime covering waste carrier registration and identifying and remedying contaminated land	If any contaminated land is discovered on site or contamination caused while on site, immediate consultation should be sought with DOE	N/A	Planning During construction Post construction

4.5   Materials

4.5.1   Environmental impact

Materials selection and use on site can have several direct and indirect environmental impacts, for instance:

Table 4.2
Example of environmental impacts

Material	Direct impacts	Indirect impacts
Timber	□ depletion of resource □ destruction of habitat □ killing of flora and fauna □ release of CO_2 from logging.	□ use of fossil fuels to cut trees and transport timber □ waste produced in further treatment and use on site □ emissions (CO_2, NOX, SOX, etc) in transport □ reduction in biodiversity.
Aggregates	□ depletion of finite resource □ pollution during extraction and processing □ visual impact and loss of land.	□ emissions (CO_2, NOX, SOX, etc) in transport □ waste generated through use.

These are two simplified examples of how commonly used construction materials can affect the environment. Most materials that are used in construction can have a negative impact on the environment and as a consequence a sustainable approach to the procurement and use of materials on site to reduce them is essential.

Construction environmental assessment schemes such as BREEAM, CEEQUAL, the Code for Sustainable Homes, DREAM and LEED consider materials selection to have a significant environmental impact on projects. Inappropriate materials selection during the construction phase is likely to affect the overall scheme award (see Section 2.5).

It is good practice to consider this link between material selection, use on site and waste management. This is referred to as resource efficiency and is the first step towards effective waste management and ultimately generating minimal waste.

This section of the guide is sub-divided into two parts to reflect construction process, site management and breadth of the topic, as follows:

☐   material procurement

☐   management of materials on site.

4.5.2   Material procurement

Important considerations when sourcing materials

Responsible sourcing and management of materials should ensure that the environmental, social and economic impacts associated with those materials are minimised.

All materials contain natural resources, whether this is direct as in timber or indirect as oil in plastics. Material manufacture may consume large amounts of natural resources such as the fuel used to maintain high temperatures in the manufacture of cement. Some materials contain hazardous chemicals or consume or release hazardous chemicals during their manufacture, application or disposal.

Where hazardous materials are being specified, alternatives with a lower environmental impact should be sought wherever possible.

Responsible sourcing considers the people involved in the abstraction or manufacture of the material or product. It is important to ensure that the human rights of these people are not being infringed through age, discrimination, welfare and working conditions.

When buying material made from natural resources such as timber it is important to ensure it is from a sustainable source. Buying Forest Stewardship Council (FSC) or PEFC (Programme for Endorsement of Forest Certification) certified timber ensures a chain of custody from tree to site and that the timber is sustainably sourced.

Timber

Timber certification is an important tool to trace the origin of the timber being procured, ensuring a chain of custody from forest to site, and providing evidence to stakeholders that timber has been procured from legal and sustainable sources (see Figure 4.16). In response to an increasing demand for verifiable sustainable sources of timber, several credible certification systems have been developed. Timber certified through the FSC scheme and PEFC is widely available in the UK. Any timber used on site should have a certified chain of custody as a minimum.

Figure 4.16
Use of FSC timber on site (courtesy Parsons Brinckerhoff)

Further guidance on purchasing timber from sustainable sources can be found in guidance by Greenpeace, Friends of the Earth and the WWF-UK Forest and Trade Network UK. Listings of FSC retailers may be found at **<www.fsc-uk.org>**.

Also refer to the UK Government site Central Point of Expertise on Timber Procurement **<www.cpet.org.uk>**

Aggregates and cement replacements

The use of recycled and secondary aggregates helps to reduce the demand for virgin quarried materials and can be a cost effective alternative. Of the aggregates used in UK each year, 70m tonnes come from recycled or secondary sources. A good example is the use of pulverised fuel ash (PFA) or furnace bottom ash (FBA) as cement replacement in concrete. Other examples are detailed in Table 4.3.

Table 4.3

Examples of recycled and secondary sources of aggregate
and cement replacements

| Recycled | Secondary | |
	Manufactured	Natural
☐ recycled aggregate (RA) ☐ recycled concrete aggregate (RCA) ☐ recycled asphalt ☐ recycled asphalt planings (RAP) ☐ spent rail ballast	☐ blast furnace slag ☐ steel slag ☐ pulverized-fuel ash (PFA) ☐ incinerator bottom ash (IBA) ☐ furnace bottom ash (FBA) ☐ used foundry sand ☐ spent oil shale ☐ recycled glass ☐ recycled plastic ☐ recycled tyres	☐ slate aggregate ☐ china clay sand ☐ colliery spoil

The Aggregates Levy (AGL) tax was introduced in the UK on 1 April 2002. It is an environmental tax that is levied on the commercial exploitation of rock, sand and gravel when used as aggregate for construction purposes. The purposes of the levy is to maximise the use of recycled aggregate and alternatives to virgin aggregate, and to promote the efficient use of virgin aggregate. The AGL is designed to encourage a shift in demand away from virgin aggregate towards recycled and secondary aggregates.

The importation, storage and placement of recycled and secondary aggregates on site requires an environmental permit, licence or exemption from the local environmental agency at all times unless the aggregate has been produced in accordance with a quality protocol, for example the Waste & Resources Action Programme (WRAP) quality protocol for the production of aggregates from inert waste. The resultant aggregate in this example is classified as a recovered non-waste product.

Further information on specifying, purchasing or supplying recycled or secondary aggregates is available from the AggRegain website <**www.aggregain.org.uk**> developed by WRAP.

Case study 4.3
On-site crushing and reuse of site-won inert
materials (courtesy Kier)

On-site crushing of inert materials, arising from demolition work, to produce fill for use on site, normally requires both space and large quantities of material for it to be feasible. However, the introduction of mini crushers has now made this operation practicable on small and constrained sites, as was demonstrated on the contract to refurbish the central square at the University of East Anglia (UEA).

Central square at the UEA is the main public circulation area, and was fully renovated in 2009. This necessitated the removal of over 1200 m² of paving slabs. By careful handling, the site team managed to salvage nearly a third of these, handing them over to the UEA Estates Department for use in repairing other areas of existing paving across the campus.

The remaining slabs and concrete bed were crushed on site, over a period of four days, using a mini-crusher. This produced 260 tonnes of clean fill material that, following testing, was later reused in the works. The result was zero waste to landfill and a significant cost saving. Crushing the concrete on site also reduced the number of vehicle movements and the carbon emissions, on what was a very restricted site.

Costs and savings

Total cost of crusher, JCB and attendance £1600 (four days @ £400 per day)

Potential cost of disposal £1560 (260 tonnes of concrete @ £6/t)

Cost of purchasing new material £3120 (260 tonnes of concrete @ £12/t)

Total saving to the project: £3080 (£3120 + £1560 – £1600)

Carbon emissions comparison

Offsite disposal, using a 20t lorry, would require thirteen 40 mile round trips

Fuel used, at 8.5 mpg, would be (40/8.5) x13 x 4.546 = 278 litres

Crusher, over four days @ four litres of fuel per hour, used 4 x 8x 4 = 128 litres

Fuel saved 150 litres, which is equal to 390 kg of CO_2 (150 x 2.6 kg CO_2/l)

For a crusher of this size, as dust suppression equipment was fitted and it was only on site for a short period, no environmental permit was required.

WRAP have developed the *Quality protocol* for the production of aggregates from inert waste to help with the use of recycled aggregates in construction. In the context of construction and within clearly defined end uses, quality protocols for PFA, steel slag, IBA, tyre derived rubber materials and tyre bales are being considered. If recycled aggregates are sourced from a supplier, and accompanied by a quality certificate and test certificates, it should have ceased to be waste and does not need to be treated as such (further details are available from the AggRegain website).

Case study 4.4
Glass sand (courtesy Balfour Beatty)

Background to the project

The A3 at Hindhead is an important scheme to tackle congestion and safety issues, and improve the environment on this busy road. It will complete the missing link in the dual carriageway between Greater London and Portsmouth. The project comprises a 6.5 km dual two-lane carriageway between Hammer Lane on the Surrey-Hampshire boundary and Boundless Lane near Thursley. Twin bored tunnels will take the A3 under a site of specific scientific interest (SSSI) adjacent to the Devil's Punchbowl.

Material used

Glass sand is a recycled aggregate made from glass bottles and jars, which can be used in the construction industry as a replacement for quarried or marine sand. Glass sand is made by crushing and screening glass waste to a particle size of 6 mm down. Glass sand is being used on the A3 as a:

☐ constituent of cement bound material (CBM) used in the construction of the lower road base for the new A3 (up to 40 per cent)

☐ filter or protective layer lining all the scheme permanent infiltration and attenuation ponds for highways drainage

☐ filter layer in the scheme permanent soakaways for highways drainage from the new A3

☐ protective layer underlying the green roof for the tunnel service buildings.

Rationale for use

The potential for using glass sand on the A3 project was identified early in the construction phase and the majority was supplied by Viridor. The Highways Agency specification allows for use of up to 40 per cent glass in the road base. The choice of recycled glass sand was made easier because there are no quarries near to the A3 project (30 mile radius) that can provide sand of a suitable quality. Neither are the Hythe sands excavated during earthworks work for the A3 earthworks fit for this purpose. The particle size of the glass sand makes it suitable for use as a filter and protective layer.

Economic and environmental benefits

☐ reduced the demand for sand or other primary aggregates that have to be quarried or dredged from estuaries

☐ reuse of glass reduces the volume of waste taken to landfill

☐ glass sand is an inert material and does not present a pollution risk

☐ reduced wastage of materials by producing CBM on-site

☐ a cost saving of £191 235 compared to quarried sand

Case study 4.4 (contd)
Glass sand (courtesy Balfour Beatty)

- □   on-site manufacture of CBM reduces potential delays from off-site production and delivery
- □   supply of the glass sand represents a cost saving to Viridor who would have to landfill the glass sand if they could not find an alternative use for material
- □   use of recycled glass sand is economical, environmentally friendly, and its use is technically feasible and provides suitable quality and performance
- □   close liaison between the contractor, designer and client allowed for appropriate and effective use of recycled glass sand on the A3 project.

Plasterboard and gypsum

Gypsum wastes are produced from plaster and plasterboard manufacture. As with all wastes, gypsum and other high sulphate wastes are considered to be hazardous only if mixed with other hazardous wastes.

New plasterboard should be stored flat, undercover and away from traffic and moisture to prevent damage to the boards resulting in it becoming waste. It is unlikely that waste plasterboard generated during demolition or refit can be recycled due to contamination and this should be segregated from general waste to reduce disposal costs.

To reduce disposal costs construction projects should seek to recycle plasterboard wastage wherever possible by arranging a take back scheme with the supplier.

From 1 April 2009, gypsum and plasterboard cannot be sent to landfill in England and Wales if mixed with biodegradable waste, they must be separated and deposited in a cell for high sulphate waste. In Scotland, SEPA allow plasterboard to be mixed with other wastes in small quantities before disposal to landfill. In Northern Ireland any non-hazardous waste containing any amount of gypsum waste sent to landfill must now go into a separate cell for high sulphate waste or to a non-hazardous landfill where no biodegradable waste is accepted. Also any gypsum based materials that are classified as hazardous waste must be disposed of in a hazardous landfill.

Non-hazardous gypsum-based and other high sulphate bearing materials should be deposited of only in landfills for non-hazardous waste in cells where no biodegradable waste is accepted. Loads containing identifiable gypsum or plasterboard must not be taken to landfill, but should be treated to remove the gypsum or plasterboard.

Polyvinyl chloride (PVC)

The construction industry is one of the largest consumers of PVC, using it extensively in applications such as piping, cladding, wiring, flooring, windows and many others. It is estimated that the construction industry consumes in the region of 500 000 tonnes per annum. The issues surrounding PVC are contentious because of the many substances used during PVC manufacture and their release during accidental fire or incineration. Alternatives to PVC should be specified wherever possible.

Formaldehyde

Formaldehyde is most commonly used as a bonding material for composite boards such as medium density fibreboard (MDF) and plywood. Also, it is used in soft furnishings and carpets, providing a degree of fire retardation. Exposure to even low levels of formaldehyde through inhalation can cause irritation to the eyes, nose, throat, mucous membranes and skin. Unsealed chipboard, plywood, fire retardants and some furnishings have been found to yield measurable quantities of formaldehyde In addition, when boards such as MDF are cut, a fine dust is created that can be respired leading to possible exposure to released formaldehyde. Formaldehyde-free and low formaldehyde containing boards and products are increasingly available in the UK and should be specified wherever possible.

4.5.3   Materials assessments

When procuring materials consideration needs to given to client and legal requirements. Traditionally these have been referred to as:

☐   preferred – with reduced environmental or social impact (eg FSC timber)

☐   advisory – not banned, but those which clients would prefer not to be used (eg PVC)

☐   prohibited – banned by law (eg asbestos).

Following the update to the *Green guide to specification* greater emphasis is being placed on Ecopoint scoring from A+ to E of main building elements, such as roof, floor or wall systems, rather that addressing materials in isolation (see BRE, 2009). It is becoming increasingly common for specification lists to state an acceptable BRE Ecopoint band such as "B" for a roofing system component, rather than to specify the avoidance of PVC. Where this is the case liaison with the material manufacturer and reference to the BRE guide is necessary.

Increasingly a life cycle analysis (or cradle to grave) approach is being taken to demonstrate the environmental impact or sustainability of products and materials. In Europe, the European Committee for Standardisation are undertaking several projects to standardise the environmental declarations of products.

The environmental impacts of materials selection are considered significant within the CEEQUAL and BREEAM assessment methodologies (see Section 2.5), and responsible sourcing of materials contributes to the overall score.

Advice should be sought from the environmental manager if clarification is required. Also see the further guidance section at the end of this chapter for sources of further information.

4.5.4   Encouraging material resource efficiency

Increasing resource efficiency and minimising waste are important for both reducing environmental impact and minimising costs. An important tool for this is the site waste management plan (SWMP), which is invaluable in identifying where opportunities for reuse and recycling can be identified before works start.

It was once common practice that an extra five to 10 per cent of materials were "over-ordered" to allow for site wastage through damage, spills, under-supply and vandalism. These figures can be reduced. The materials resource efficiency checklist can be used to focus on how materials are ordered, delivered, stored and handled on site and to help investigate how to reduce waste.

Packaging plays an important role in materials and product protection and ease of handling on site: too little increases product waste, too much increases packaging waste. Early engagement with the materials supplier will maximise opportunities to reduce the amount of waste material and packaging. Reductions can be found from the adoption of "just in time" deliveries and use of appropriately packaged goods for the site requirements. Opportunities to reduce waste also exist through material and packaging recycling and take back schemes. Most suppliers will be subject to the requirements of the Packaging Regulations 2009 and should be able to offer alternatives if excess package becomes waste on site.

4.5.5   Management of materials on site

Storing materials

The correct storage of materials is necessary to ensure they are:

☐   located away from sensitive receptors, eg watercourses, including drainage and transport routes

☐   unlikely to pollute: all potentially polluting materials should be stored on impermeable and bunded areas

☐   not at risk of theft, vandalism or accidental damage

☐   not spoiled through exposure to the elements

☐   not subject to double handling – the more times materials are moved the more likely it is that damage will occur

☐   easily accessible.

For guidance on effective storage of materials on site refer to the materials storage checklist.

Managing materials

Different materials need to be managed in different ways according to their potential environmental impacts. For example, if oil is stored in England and Scotland, it must be done so in accordance with the Oils Storage Regulations (2001 and 2006 respectively). These regulations require that oil containers are strong enough and that they are unlikely to burst or leak during ordinary use (in Scotland only application for portable oil containers with a capacity less than 200 litres), containers must be within a drip tray, bund or other secondary containment system and must be located away from any watercourses (see Section 4.9.3).

These Regulations do not apply in Northern Ireland and Wales, but consideration should be given to meeting such requirements, as they are designed to prevent contamination of the water environment that would be an offence under other legislation. Use the checklists provided in this section to ensure good practice with oil fuel storage and management, but be sure to check <**www.netregs.gov.uk**> for specific legal requirements in the site's region.

Many materials that are potentially hazardous such as adhesives, solvents, paints and curing agents are regulated under the Control of Substances Hazardous to Health (COSHH) Regulations. Details of how these materials have to be stored, used and disposed of are stipulated in the COSHH datasheets, which should be followed. Copies of the datasheets and an inventory of all COSHH materials held on site should be maintained. As a minimum all COSHH materials should be kept in a secure bunded COSHH store located away from drains and watercourses.

Defra has published a groundwater protection code: solvent use and storage under the Groundwater Regulations 1998. Copies of this code of practice can be downloaded from the Defra website <**www.defra.gov.uk**>.

Figure 4.17
Storage of fuel oil and chemicals (courtesy Parsons Brinckerhoff)

For all other materials, consider the appropriate means to handle products/materials to prevent them being damaged and becoming waste. For instance, storage on pallets in designated areas and protected from the elements (eg wind and rain).

Stockpiling

For any stockpile that will be used on site for a long period, it is worth considering profiling and vegetating it to improve its stability and aesthetics (see managing stockpiles checklist), so as not to generate a nuisance from dust. Ensure control measures are in place to deal with silt runoff during wet conditions and dust during dry periods. Soil stockpiles or areas of exposed soil should be managed to prevent silty runoff from entering watercourses, drains, public highways and areas of the site where materials are stored. This can be done through bunding, vegetation, silt fencing and through the use of cut-off trenches, berms and bunds. Consideration should be given to the need for an environmental permit or waste management exemption.

Materials such as uncontaminated spoil arising from site set-up, sands and gravel excavations (see Section 2.2) can be used to create a temporary bund or acoustic barrier while works are in progress. Where the bund or barrier is situated needs careful consideration as does the need to comply with environmental permitting requirements.

Figure 4.18
Landscaped stockpile of spoil (courtesy Galliford Try)

Case study 4.5
Reuse of natural stone and other on-site recycling
initiatives (courtesy Morrison Construction)

Construction of 120 m of natural stone clad reinforced concrete flood defence wall near to a small village hamlet. The site was located in a conservation area, which meant the wall had to be remade using existing stone on site or local stone sourced nearby. An existing stone shed had to be dismantled and rebuilt as part of the works.

As part of the reconstruction of the wall about 300 m² of Natural York Stone walling was removed, cleaned, stored and reconstructed in exactly the same position and size without any damage being caused. This meant that no new materials had to be ordered or offsite recycling undertaken. In addition the supporting wood beam from the stone shed was preserved and reused in the new structure. Surplus excavated material was used to reinforce the existing flood bund. Undamaged pallets used to deliver bricks and other materials were registered with a pallet collection scheme and collected every month. The site used on-site canteen and office recycling facilities for cans, paper, cardboard, plastic and glass, which was collected weekly.

4.5.6 Good practice checklists

 Ordering materials

Try to substitute hazardous materials with non-hazardous alternatives

Try to replace virgin materials (eg aggregates) with recycled products

Try to order products with recycled content

Try to source ethically-produced materials

Order sustainably sourced materials, such as FSC timber or PEFC timber or procure products certified to the framework of BES 6001

Consider the environmental impact of the material life cycle

Consider transport distances of materials: can products be sourced locally?

 Resource efficiency

Try to only order the required amount

Order materials cut to size to reduce off-cuts

Establish "just in time" systems so that materials are not stored on site unnecessarily, reducing potential damage

When deliveries arrive on site:
- ☐ ensure deliveries are off-loaded in a designated area of site
- ☐ do not accept delivery of damaged goods
- ☐ ensure goods are checked that they are the correct specification, quantity

When handling materials, avoid:
- ☐ damage or spillage through incorrect or repetitive handling.

Use of aggregates on site

Ensure suitability for use:

☐ make sure that materials do not contain contaminants and that pH levels are suitable for use where the site is located. This can be achieved by undertaking:

☐ an accredited laboratory analysis of any contaminants present

☐ leachate tests for the contaminants identified.

Consultation:

☐ the environmental regulator has a remit to protect groundwater sources from contamination and must be consulted before any recycled materials are used in the ground. *Note: recycled aggregates under the WRAP quality protocol need no authorisation from the Environment Agency for use. Other waste materials can be registered as exempt if within exemption limits*

☐ the laboratory results should be sent to the local environmental regulator's technical team for approval to ensure that local conditions do not prevent the use of such materials.

Materials storage

Store all containers of materials, such as oils and paints, in a bunded area

Designate responsibility for hazardous materials storage, restrict and manage access

Clearly mark the area(s)

Store materials in suitable containers that are labelled appropriately with fitted lids, taps and tops in good condition

Put control measures in place and/or locate spill kits near to bulk stores and ensure they are accessible and fully stocked

Store material so as to guard against breakage, vandalism or theft

Protect stores against flood damage or inundation

Store waste in a designated area away from the materials storage

Managing stockpiles

Store topsoil for reuse in piles less than 2 m high to prevent damage to the soil structure	
Segregate different grades of soil	
Position spoil and temporary stockpiles away from watercourses and drainage systems	
Minimise movements of materials in stockpiles to reduce degradation of the soil structure	
Silty water formed by erosion of the stockpile should be managed correctly	
Direct surface water away from the stockpiles to prevent erosion at the bottom	
Place silt screens around spoil heaps to trap silt from any surface water runoff	
Vegetate long-term stockpiles to prevent dust in dry weather conditions, and reduce erosion of the stockpile to form silty runoff. Ensure adequate weed control	

 Refuelling protocol

Designate a bunded refuelling area, away from site drains	
Avoid using remote fill points. Where these are unavoidable install suitable oil separators to the surface drainage system	
Avoid refuelling close to watercourses. Where this is unavoidable keep materials such as absorbent pads or booms readily available in case of spillage	
All refuelling should be supervised. Do not leave valves open unattended (note that auto-close valves may be a legal requirement)	
Keep an emergency spill kit at each refuelling point. If mobile refuelling is carried out, ensure each bowser carries a spill kit	
Bowsers should have an automatic cut out and should be locked when not in use	
Ensure that personnel carrying out refuelling are aware of the protocol and know what actions to take in an emergency	

Storing oils, fuels and chemicals

Securely store all containers that contain potential pollutants (eg fuels, oils and chemicals) according to oil storage legislation	
Label containers clearly so that appropriate remedial action can be taken in the event of a spillage	
All bulk fuel storage should be contained within a double skinned bowser or container or have a bund	
Regularly check taps and hoses for leakage and signs of damage	
Avoid storing drums tightly against each other. Store drums so that they can all be inspected for leaks	
Prevent damage from vandalism. Ensure that all valves and trigger guns are vandal and tamper proof	
Display a notice that demands valves and trigger guns are to be locked when not in use	
Store tanks or drums in a secure bunded container or compound that is locked when not in use	
Fuel, oil and chemicals should be stored on an impermeable base (this may be part of a bund). Ideally, such materials should be stored away from areas of groundwater contamination risk. This should be identified in the contract but may be worth discussing with the environmental agencies	
Provide separate fill pipes for each tank unless the tanks are interconnected by a balance pipe of greater flow capacity than the fill pipe	
Mark fill pipes with the product type and a tank number where there is more than one tank	
Before moving a drum, check the bung is secure	

Bunding tanks

To avoid accidental spillage, bund tanks with a minimum capacity of 110 per cent of the volume of the largest tank or 25 per cent of the total storage capacity, whichever is the greater	
Do not allow bunded areas to fill with rainwater or slops (ideally, provide a cover). Empty and dispose of any water collected in an appropriate way	
Site tanks away from vehicle movements and mark them clearly so that people know they are a potential risk	
Do not put tanks where there is a direct link to surface drains, watercourses or sewers. Avoid placing tanks on unpaved ground, to reduce the risk of soil contamination. Protect tanks from vandalism	
The bund should be impermeable to the substance that is being stored in the tank	
Position air vent pipes so that they can be seen easily and directed so that any discharge (eg in the event of the tank being overfilled) is directed down into the bund	
Fill points should be inside the bund	
Fit any pumps sited outside the bund with a non-return/check valve installed in the feed line	

4.5.7   Further guidance

ANDERSON, J and SHIERS, D (2009) *The Green Guide to Specification*, fourth edition, Wiley-Blackwell, London (ISBN: 978-1405119610)

BRE (2009) Environmental and framework standard: *Framework standard for the responsible sourcing of construction products*, BES 6001 Issue 2, Building Research Establishment, Watford *

BSI (2001) SA 8000: *Social Accountability Standard*, British Standards Institute, London

ENVIRONMENT AGENCY, SEPA, NIEA (2010) Pollution Prevention Guidelines (PPG) 2: *Above ground oil storage tanks* *

ENVIRONMENT AGENCY, SEPA, EHSNI (2004) Pollution Prevention Guidelines (PPG) 26: *Storage and handling of drums and intermediate bulk containers* *

DEFRA (2004) *Groundwater protection code: Solvent use and storage*, Department for Environment, Food and Rural Affairs, London *

GUTHRIE, P, WOOLVERIDGE, A C and COVENTRY, S (1998) *Managing materials and components on site*, SP146, CIRIA, London (ISBN: 978-0-86017-481-3)

HM GOVERNMENT (2008) *Strategy for Sustainable Construction*, Department for Business Innovation and Skills, London *

HSE (1998) *Chemical warehousing: The storage of packaged dangerous substances*, HSG71 (second edition), HSE Books, London (ISBN: 0-71761-484-0)

HSE (1998) *The storage of flammable liquids in containers*, HSE Books, London (ISBN: 978-0-71761-471-4)

KWAN, J *et al* (1997) *Ground engineering spoil: good management practice*, R179, CIRIA, London (ISBN: 978-0-86017-484-4)

LONDON DEVELOPMENT AGENCY (2007) *The Mayor of London's Green Procurement Code*. Go to:

*   denotes that a copy of the document is included on the accompanying resource CD

Relevant toolbox talks (refer to Appendix A4)

Spill control

Dust and air quality

Oil/diesel storage

Material handling and housekeeping

Bentonite

Segregation of waste

4.5.8   Legislation

The following table is a brief summary of applicable legislation to materials, including requirements and divided by UK region. Due to frequent legislative developments users should check <**www.netregs.gov.uk**> when using the table.

Legislation	Key requirements	Direct site requirements	Indirect requirements	Application time planning/during construction/post
England				
Control of Substances Hazardous to Health Regulations 2002 (as amended)	The organisation: □ shall ensure that the exposure of its employees to substances hazardous to health is either prevented or, where this is not reasonably practicable, adequately controlled □ that provides any control measure, personal protective equipment or other thing or facility pursuant to these Regulations shall take all reasonable steps to ensure that it is properly used or applied as specified □ that provides any control measure shall ensure that it is maintained in an efficient state, in efficient working order and in good repair. Personal protective equipment should be in a clean condition □ shall ensure that employees who are or are liable to be exposed to a hazardous substance are under suitable health surveillance □ shall prepare procedures, provide information and establish warning systems to deal with an emergency in the workplace related to the presence of a substance hazardous to health	Ensure all substances hazardous to health are stored, maintained and handled in accordance with site specific risk assessments, and are carried out before materials are brought on to site	Check contractors on site have risk assessments and COSHH documentation for any hazardous materials brought on to site	Planning During construction

Legislation	Key requirements	Direct site requirements	Indirect requirements	Application time planning/during construction/post
The Registration, Evaluation, Authorisation and Restriction of Chemicals (REACH) Enforcement Regulations 2008	If chemicals are used on site that are not common check with the supplier to see if they comply with the REACH regulations. Safety data sheets should be provided with each chemical kept on site: these will be provided by the supplier. All safety data sheets should be kept with the appropriate chemical and the recommended risk assessments checked for feasibility on the site for storage and use. If the risk assessment is not adequate for use on site a new risk assessment should be carried out and documented	Ensure safety data sheets are kept with all appropriate chemicals stored and used on site and that risk assessments have been studied or amended	N/A	Planning During construction
Control of Pollution (Oil Storage) (England) Regulations 2001	Imposes general requirements for preventing pollution of controlled waters from oil storage, particularly fixed tanks, drums or mobile bowsers. The legislation applies to the storage of 200 litres or more of oil of any kind, including petrol, but excluding the storage of waste oil. Restrictions also govern the use of pumps. It details requirements for oil stored in tanks, drums, mobile browsers or underground that must be identified and implemented, and makes contravention a criminal offence	Bowsers that are not self-bunded must be kept in a bunded area of 110 per cent capacity when in use. A drip tray with a capacity of 25 per cent is acceptable for single drums. Oil tanks must have appropriate secondary containment, the containment capacity must be a minimum of 25 per cent of the total capacity or 110 per cent of the largest tank, whichever is greatest	N/A	Planning During construction

Legislation	Key requirements	Direct site requirements	Indirect requirements	Application time planning/during construction/post
Wales				
Control of Substances Hazardous to Health Regulations 2002 (as amended)	The organisation: ☐ shall ensure that the exposure of its employees to substances hazardous to health is either prevented or, where this is not reasonably practicable, adequately controlled ☐ that provides any control measure, personal protective equipment or other thing or facility pursuant to these Regulations shall take all reasonable steps to ensure that it is properly used or applied as specified that provides any control measure shall ensure that it is maintained in an efficient state, in efficient working order and in good repair. Personal protective equipment should be in a clean condition ☐ shall ensure that employees who are or are liable to be exposed to a hazardous substance are under suitable health surveillance ☐ shall prepare procedures, provide information and establish warning systems to deal with an emergency in the workplace related to the presence of a substance hazardous to health	Ensure all substances hazardous to health are stored, maintained and handled in accordance with site specific risk assessments to be carried out before materials are brought on site	Check contractors on site have risk assessments and COSHH documentation for any hazardous materials brought on site	Planning During construction

Legislation	Key requirements	Direct site requirements	Indirect requirements	Application time planning/during construction/post
The Registration, Evaluation, Authorisation and Restriction of Chemicals (REACH) Enforcement Regulations 2008	If using chemicals on site that are not common check with the supplier to see if they comply with the REACH regulations Safety data sheets should be provided with each chemical kept on site; these will be provided by the supplier. All safety data sheets should be kept with the appropriate chemical and the recommended risk assessments checked for feasibility on the site for storage and use. If the risk assessment is not adequate for use on site a new risk assessment should be carried out and documented	Ensure safety data sheets are kept with all appropriate chemicals stored and used on site and that risk assessments have been studied or amended	N/A	Planning During construction

Legislation	Key requirements	Direct site requirements	Indirect requirements	Application time planning/during construction/post
Scotland				
Control of Substances Hazardous to Health Regulations 2002 (as amended)	The organisation: ☐ shall ensure that the exposure of its employees to substances hazardous to health is either prevented or, where this is not reasonably practicable, adequately controlled ☐ that provides any control measure, personal protective equipment or other thing or facility pursuant to these Regulations shall take all reasonable steps to ensure that it is properly used or applied as the case may be ☐ that provides any control measure shall ensure that it is maintained in an efficient state, in efficient working order and in good repair. Personal protective equipment should be in a clean condition ☐ shall ensure that employees who are or are liable to be exposed to a hazardous substance are under suitable health surveillance ☐ shall prepare procedures, provide information and establish warning systems to deal with an emergency in the workplace related to the presence of a substance hazardous to health	Ensure all substances hazardous to health are stored, maintained and handled in accordance with site specific risk assessments to be carried out before materials are brought on site	Check contractors on site have risk assessments and COSHH documentation for any hazardous materials brought on site	Planning During construction

Legislation	Key requirements	Direct site requirements	Indirect requirements	Application time planning/during construction/post
	If using chemicals on site that are not common check with the supplier to see if they comply with the REACH regulations			
The Registration, Evaluation, Authorisation and Restriction of Chemicals (REACH) Enforcement Regulations 2008	Safety data sheets should be provided with each chemical kept on site, these will be provided by the supplier. All safety data sheets should be kept with the appropriate chemical and the recommended risk assessments checked for feasibility on the site for storage and use. If the risk assessment is not adequate for use on site a new risk assessment should be carried out and documented	Ensure safety data sheets are kept with all appropriate chemicals stored and used on site and that risk assessments have been studied or amended	N/A	Planning During construction

Legislation	Key requirements	Direct site requirements	Indirect requirements	Application time planning/during construction/post
Water Environment (Oil Storage) (Scotland) Regulations 2006	Where oil is stored in any portable container with a storage capacity of less than 200 litres, the container must be of sufficient strength and structural integrity to ensure that it is unlikely to burst or leak in its ordinary use Where the container has a storage capacity of 200 litres or more, the regulations require provision of a secondary containment (a bund or drip-tray) to ensure that any leaking or spilt oil cannot enter the water environment	A secondary containment system (bund or drip tray) must be provided to catch any oil leaking from the container or its ancillary pipe work and equipment The container must be situated within a secondary containment system (eg bund, drip tray) of sufficient capacity to contain at least 110 per cent of the maximum contents of the container. Where more than one container is stored, the bund should be capable of storing at least 110 per cent of the largest tank or 25 per cent of the total storage capacity, whichever is the greater (in the case of drums the tray/bund size should be at least 25 per cent of total storage capacity) Oil stored in mobile bowsers is also required to be bunded The bund base and walls must be impermeable to water and oil and checked regularly for leaks	N/A	Planning During construction

Legislation	Key requirements	Direct site requirements	Indirect requirements	Application time planning/during construction/post
Northern Ireland				
Control of Substances Hazardous to Health Regulations (Northern Ireland) 2003 (as amended)	The organisation: ☐ shall ensure that the exposure of its employees to substances hazardous to health is either prevented or, where this is not reasonably practicable, adequately controlled ☐ that provides any control measure, personal protective equipment or other thing or facility pursuant to these Regulations shall take all reasonable steps to ensure that it is properly used or applied as the case may be ☐ that provides any control measure shall ensure that it is maintained in an efficient state, in efficient working order and in good repair. Personal protective equipment should be in a clean condition ☐ shall ensure that employees who are or are liable to be exposed to a hazardous substance are under suitable health surveillance ☐ shall prepare procedures, provide information and establish warning systems to deal with an emergency in the workplace related to the presence of a substance hazardous to health	Ensure all substances hazardous to health are stored, maintained and handled in accordance with site specific risk assessments to be carried out before materials are brought on to site	Check contractors on site have risk assessments and COSHH documentation for any hazardous materials brought onto site	Planning During construction

Legislation	Key requirements	Direct site requirements	Indirect requirements	Application time planning/during construction/post
	If using chemicals on site that are not common check with the supplier to see if they comply with the REACH regulations			
The Registration, Evaluation, Authorisation and Restriction of Chemicals (REACH) Enforcement Regulations 2008	Safety data sheets should be provided with each chemical kept on site, these will be provided by the supplier. All safety data sheets should be kept with the appropriate chemical and the recommended risk assessments checked for feasibility on the site for storage and use. If the risk assessment is not adequate for use on site a new risk assessment should be carried out and documented	Ensure safety data sheets are kept with all appropriate chemicals stored and used on site and that risk assessments have been studied or amended	N/A	Planning During construction

4.6   Noise and vibration

4.6.1   Why is noise and vibration management important?

Excessive noise on site not only represents a major hazard to site workers but can annoy neighbours and in some cases disturb nearby wildlife. Excessive noise and vibration can cause the following:

☐   poor quality of life for affected residents (ie disturbance and stress)

☐   complaints

☐   structural damage to buildings and utilities

☐   wildlife disturbance.

And lead to:

☐   statutory enforcement of controls by the local authority or court, including revisions to working methods, working hours and even stopping the works

☐   programme delays and associated costs

☐   damage to third party and community relations

☐   damage to corporate/project reputation

☐   damage to wildlife habitats.

Effective planning, and on-site management of noise, will significantly reduce the likelihood of any of these actions being taken, and so reduce the risk of construction noise affecting the overall performance of a project. Understanding, adopting, communicating and integrating the legal requirement to employ best practicable means (BPM) to minimise noise and vibration at all times and all locations, is the best way to indicate to the local authorities, local residents and construction personnel that noise and vibration is being managed satisfactorily on site.

Excessive noise is the single most common source of complaint against the construction industry, and can result in work being stopped on site.

4.6.2 What is noise?

Noise is commonly referred to as unwanted sound. Sound is a wave transmitted as small changes in air pressure (known as sound pressure) between a source and receiver (ie a construction site and a nearby resident) occur.

Noise units

The measure of sound pressure level is the decibel (dB) and it is based on a logarithmic scale. A sound level meter is used to measure noise and can measure different parameters and weighting. The A-weighting scale is often used as it corresponds most closely to the frequency response of the human ear. Advice should be sought from a qualified acoustic consultant with regard to the relevant parameters to measure and the type of assessment required.

Propagation

The level of noise observed from a construction activity at a nearby building depends on several factors, some of which can be controlled on site while others are rely on local conditions. To manage noise on site, consideration should be given to those factors that can be controlled, namely:

☐ the noise level of the activity (determined by construction method and plant selection)

☐ level of screening between the noise source and the receiver point

☐ location of the activity within the construction site (if possible).

Local conditions that cannot normally be controlled on site are:

☐ distance from the noise source to the building

☐ reflections from nearby buildings

☐ ground absorption

☐ atmospheric conditions (ie wind direction, humidity and temperature).

Case study 4.6
Noise monitoring undertaken as best practice on
the A421 (courtesy Balfour Beatty)

The project works that stretch over 13 km are near to both dense and sparsely populated areas that have been subject to noise monitoring. Noise monitoring is undertaken by the site environment team to ensure the project is abiding to limits set by the local authority environment health officer (EHO).

Monitoring is undertaken both during the day as well as at night to ensure the levels do not disturb residents.

In the event of work being required outside of normal working hours, a request is submitted to the EHO at least seven days in advance detailing what works and equipment will be used as well as indicating the location. If necessary further mitigation will be implemented such as screens and or curtailing work at an agreed time as to minimise disturbance.

Effective planning

Careful planning of the construction works to take all reasonable and practicable steps to minimise noise and vibration, can significantly reduce the amount of disturbance and reduce the risk of noise abatement action. The best approach is to ensure that the legal requirement to employ BPM is understood by all staff and is integrated into the planning of all activities at all locations and at all times.

Best practicable means (BPM)

BPM as defined within Section 72 of CoPA 1974, and similarly Section 79(9) of the EPA 1990, states that:

1   This section shall apply for the construction of references in this Part of the Act to best practicable means.

2   In that expression "practicable" means reasonably practicable having regard among other thing to the local conditions and circumstances, to the current state of technical knowledge and to the financial implications.

3   The means to be employed include the design, installation, maintenance and manner and periods of operation of plant and machinery, and the design, construction and maintenance of buildings and acoustic structures.

4   The test of practicable means is to apply only so far is compatible with any duty imposed by law, and in particular is to apply to statutory

undertakers only so far as compatible with the duties imposed upon them in their capacity of statutory undertakers.

5   The said test is to apply only so far as compatible with the safety and safe working conditions, and with the exigencies of any emergency or unforeseen circumstances.

6   Subject to the preceding provisions of this section, regard shall be had, in construing references to "best practicable means", to any relevant provision of a code of practice approved under the preceding section."

This is interpreted as the balancing of noise and vibration mitigation against:

☐   cost (Clause 2)

☐   engineering practicability (Clause 3)

☐   current state of technical knowledge/techniques (Clause 2)

☐   duration (Clause 3)

☐   proximity of the works to residents (Clause 2)

☐   number of residents affected (Clause 2)

☐   time of day (Clause 3)

☐   safety (Clause 5).

As BPM is a balancing of factors, it means that noise mitigation or working constraints can be prioritised to those locations and activities, which are most required. For example:

☐   proximity of works to residents – the further away from residents works occur the less mitigation is required to demonstrate BPM (eg 500 m away opposed to only 50 m)

☐   duration – if an activity is required to be undertaken only for a few days, then it would require significantly less mitigation than if it was to be undertaken for several weeks

☐   time of day – works undertaken at night require more mitigation and justification than works during the day

☐   engineering practicability and safety – if there is no alternative but to undertake the works at night with noisy equipment (because there is no quieter equipment that exists to do the work) then this would constitute BPM, as long as detailed justification was given and local residents were informed in advance of the works.

The following generic measures should be considered in the pursuance of BPM, in order of priority:

☐ control of noise at source

☐ selection of low noise methods, eg vibro-piling

☐ control of working hours

☐ selection of quiet or low noise equipment

☐ location of equipment on site

☐ correct orientation of plant and equipment, ie ensure piling rig is facing away from sensitive receptors during impact piling operations

☐ provision of acoustic enclosures

☐ screening

☐ local screening of plant

☐ site perimeter hoarding

☐ create a one-way system to prevent unnecessary traffic movements.

If noisy activities have to be undertaken near residents over long periods then consideration can be given under BPM to provide protection. For example sound insulation to windows and ventilation at properties or temporary relocation of residents as a last resort. These approaches will be considered as BPM in law only if it can be demonstrated that all other forms of BPM (eg noise control at source) have been exhausted.

4.6.3   Control of noise at source

Selection of low noise methods

The best way to minimise the possible disturbance to residents is to minimise the amount of noise generated in the first place, ideally by selection of low noise generating methods. Some of the construction activities that cause the greatest problems are:

☐ piling (particularly by diesel hammer)

☐ breaking out with pneumatic tools

☐ scabbling of concrete

☐ falling ball demolition

☐ grit-blasting

☐ hydro-demolition.

These methods should be used only when all other practicable methods have been investigated and discounted or when their use minimises other environmental impacts. For example, hydro-demolition is noisy but the level of dust produced in comparison to conventional demolition methods is significantly less. So in certain situations it may be preferable to prioritise the control of dust rather than noise.

Working hours

The level of disturbance resulting from noise associated with a construction site activity is dependent on when and where the noise occurs. In residential areas people are more sensitive to noise in the evening, at night, at the weekend or on a bank holiday, compared to the normal working week. So, wherever possible works should be limited to weekday daytime only.

In certain industrial/office areas, where the nearby properties are unoccupied during the evening and at the weekend, it may be better to programme noisy activities for during these periods.

For mixed residential and office buildings consider "quiet periods" during the daytime when certain noisy activities (eg piling) are not undertaken to minimise the effect on the office buildings. To balance the loss of daytime hours, work into the early evening or begin works earlier.

To limit the impact of a project on the local community, the local authority will stipulate the hours that noisy works are permitted, or it may restrict working hours by placing a limit on the average noise allowed over a given period (see section on prior consent). In these cases, if the noise exceeds the limit set, the working period should be reduced or an alternative and quieter work method adopted.

BS 5228-1:2008 describes the detailed calculations needed to work out the noise levels caused by a particular project. Further guidance is given in Wills and Churcher (1999).

Selection of quiet or low noise equipment

For many construction activities there are several items of plant that could be used to undertake a particular task, eg use of hydraulic jack method over impact drop hammer. In some circumstances the use of a single larger item of equipment rather than several small items of equipment can reduce noise levels on site, eg use of a single generator opposed to several smaller generators. Ensure all plant and equipment is well maintained and is turned off when not in use.

Provision of acoustic enclosures

Some equipment can be supplied with acoustic enclosures, such as hoods and doors on compressors and generators, or other noise control devices such as jackets on pneumatic drills and shrouds on piling rigs and cranes. These devices should not only be closed but also be tight fitting and well sealed. A partly closed door is of little use.

Screening

If designed and used correctly, screening can considerably reduce noise levels from a site and at relatively low cost. Screening can be provided by existing buildings, earth bunds, site material storage, site security hoarding, or purpose built noise screens. As a general rule any screening should be placed as close as possible to either the source or receiver for maximum effect.

To screen a receiver from a noise source, there should be no "line of sight" between the source and the receiver. The amount of noise reduction provided by screening depends on two factors:

1   The increase in distance between a noise source and receiver over (or around) a noise screen compared to the direct distance path, (known as path difference) that can be expressed as path difference = (distance A + distance B) − distance C.

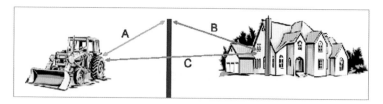

The following examples indicate where to place a noise screen to achieve the greatest noise reduction.

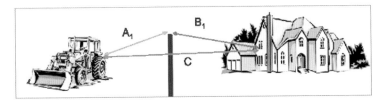

Noise screen 1 Midway between source and receiver

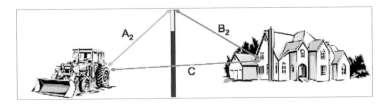

Noise screen 2 Same as Noise screen 1 but with the barrier height increased

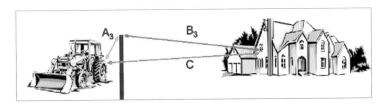

Noise screen 3 Same as Noise screen 1 but closer to the noise source

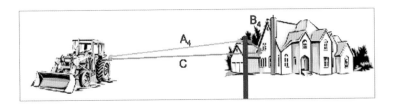

Noise screen 4 Same as Noise screen 1 but closer to the nearby residence

2   Noise screens 3 and 4 provide the best level of noise reduction as they are close to either the source or the receptor. Because the height of the barrier is lower there is a cost saving compared to screens 1 and 2. So Screens 3 and 4 are the most efficient in achieving BPM.

The amount of sound passing through the noise screen is controlled by:

a   Density of the screen material (generally the higher the density the lower the level of sound passing through the barrier)

b   Any holes/openings within the noise screen.

Generally the maximum reduction in noise level by a purpose-built screen or site security hoarding is 10 dB(A). This can be achieved by the provision of a screen that breaks the line of sight between the source(s) and receiver, and should be constructed from a material of density 7 kg/m² or higher such as:

☐   12 mm (minimum) plywood

☐   12 mm (minimum) chipboard

☐   7 mm Plexiglas.

When there are no foundations to construct a screen on then it may be possible to mount 12 mm plywood board from a frame supported by concrete "jersey" blocks (taking care not to leave a gap by shaping the frame to reach the ground between blocks).

Any gaps in the screen will significantly reduce the performance in reducing noise. It is common to construct the screen from two sheets of 12 mm board, which should be overlapped to ensure that there are minimal gaps between the sheets. If a single sheet is to be used then careful sealing of the abutting sheets is required. The gap between the layers of a double-sheeted screen can be filled with a sound-absorbing material, such as mineral wool quilt, to prevent the build-up of reverberant sound.

4.6.4   Specific BPM measures to minimise noise and vibration

Specific mitigation measures, which should adopted where appropriate to demonstrate BPM, involve:

☐   careful selection of equipment, construction methods and programming with the objective of reducing noise and vibration wherever possible. Only equipment, including road vehicles, conforming to relevant national or international standards, directives and recommendations on noise and vibration emissions, should be used

☐ using noise-control equipment such as jackets, shrouds, hoods, and doors, and ensuring they are closed (see provision of acoustic enclosures)

☐ erecting hoardings or screens as noise barriers before any construction activities are undertaken

☐ locating plant, as far as is reasonably practicable, away from receptors or as close as possible to noise barriers or hoardings where these are located between the source and receptor (see provision of acoustic enclosures)

☐ using solid doors and gates that should not be located opposite sensitive receptors. The operation of gates should be controlled to minimise the time they are open for the passage of vehicles, reducing stray noise emissions

☐ ensuring that all plant is maintained regularly to comply with relevant national or international standards

☐ ensuring that airlines are maintained and checked regularly to prevent leaks

☐ operating plant in the mode of operation that minimises noise emissions

☐ ensuring that plant is shut down when not in use

☐ prohibiting works vehicles waiting or queuing on the public highway

☐ constructing temporary infrastructure (eg haul roads) of materials that minimise noise and vibration (eg laying a tarmac surface)

☐ avoiding percussive piling, except where there is an overriding justification

☐ using bending as opposed to percussion methods to break out concrete. Rotary drills and bursters actuated by hydraulic or electrical power should be used for excavating hard material

☐ handling all materials, particularly steelwork, in a manner that minimises noise. For example storing materials as far as possible away from sensitive receptors and using resilient mats around steel handling areas

☐ designing all audible warning systems and alarms to minimise noise. Non-audible warning systems shall be used in preference, ie cab-mounted CCTV or the use of banksmen. If required, ensure that audible warning systems are switched to the minimum setting required by the HSE, and where practicable use "white noise" reversing alarms in place of the usual "siren" style reversing alert

☐   designing haul routes to minimise the amount of reversing required

☐   selecting electrically powered plant that is quieter than diesel or petrol-driven plant, if interchangeable

☐   fitting suitable anti-vibration mountings where practicable, to rotating and/or impacting equipment.

Consent

For some construction projects especially projects in residential/built up areas, it is advisable to make an application for consent under Section 61 of the Control of Pollution Act (CoPA) 1974 to the relevant local authority before works begin. The advantages of applying for a Section 61 consent are:

☐   the project can programme works without the risk of local authority intervention

☐   the risk of delay costs due to abatement action can be reduced

☐   the formal acceptance by the local authority that BPM has been adopted.

A breach of the conditions under Section 61 consent can lead to the following actions:

1   The local authority can serve a notice under Section 60 of CoPA 1974 or a nuisance abatement notice under Section 80 of the Environmental Protection Act 1990 on the project.

2   Regardless of compliance to Section 61 a resident can request a magistrate to make an abatement order under Section 82 of the Environmental Protection Act 1990. However, this is rare given that the normal procedure is for complaints to go to the local authority.

It should be noted that the adoption and employment of BPM is a defence against such a notice but if the construction method and mitigation has not been agreed with the local authority a notice may still be served.

4.6.5   Pre-construction noise monitoring

Before the works start the ambient and background noise levels at locations around the site should be monitored as part of a noise survey. The results should be used to plan the location of noisy operations that could cause nuisance to sensitive receptors, and can be used to oppose any unsubstantiated complaints.

On-site management

On-site management should continue beyond the planning stage taking the good practices and BPM measures identified to minimise noise and vibration, and ensuring that they are adopted on site. It is important to note that Section 61 and Section 60 of CoPA 1974 relate to the need to define the construction method and steps to minimise noise and vibration.

Note that the legislation relates to the actual construction methods. Noise on site should be managed through:

☐ inspections ensuring that BPM has been adopted (eg correct working hours)

☐ monitoring to confirm noise level of site activities

☐ identifying and reporting non-BPM practices, so they can be rectified

☐ revising working practices to ensure that BPM is adopted at all times

☐ repeating inspections at regular intervals during the project, but more frequently during particularly noisy activities.

Community liaison should be undertaken in advance of any noisy works. This will provide information on what activities will be carried out on site, the reasons why these works are needed and the duration of noisy activities.

Information should be sought from the community concerning sensitive periods (eg school exams), so works can be planned outside these times. If working times have been agreed, it is important to ensure that these are adhered to. Through developing and maintaining good relations, the potential for complaints or civil claims in the long-term should be reduced.

It is important to remind site personnel of their obligation to minimise noise and vibration on site. It is especially important to avoid unexpected early morning starts. This can be achieved in the site inductions, toolbox talks and through signage onsite.

4.6.6 Construction noise monitoring

During construction, regular inspections should be undertaken to ensure that the noise and vibration minimising methods, plant and mitigation identified in the planning stage are adopted on site and are working effectively.

Formal inspections should be undertaken by operatives at all times. It may occur at the same frequency and in conjunction with any health and safety review (probably once a week). If applicable, it is recommended that construction method inspections should be integrated into any health and safety or quality surveillance regime.

Environmental noise monitoring

The need to undertake noise monitoring may be a requirement of the contract or it may arise out of a consent agreement with the local authority. Although CoPA is mainly used in relation to construction site noise, the provisions of the Environmental Protection Act 1990 must also be taken into account.

It is recommended that noise monitoring be undertaken at the start of each new activity. This may mean that monitoring is required on a daily basis during the first weeks of a construction project but, subject to satisfactory results, this could be relaxed to once a week/twice-weekly depending upon the site activities. The frequency should be increased again if particularly noisy activities (such as driven piling) are undertaken.

The monitoring data can be used to assess compliance with any noise limits specified within a Section 60 notice, noise level predictions within a Section 61 consent application, or change in noise levels compared with any pre-construction noise monitoring.

The duration of the monitoring on any one day is important. BS 5228-1:2009 suggests that the average noise level over a day can be approximated within certain tolerances by taking short-term measurements throughout the day, eg five minutes in every hour.

Environmental noise monitoring should be undertaken only by suitably-trained and experienced personnel. The following information is given to help site personnel ensure monitoring is being properly carried out.

How and where to measure

A suitably qualified acoustic consultant, or suitably qualified company employee, should be employed to provide technical advice and define where and when to measure.

In sensitive areas noise measurement may be specified as a contract requirement. It is good practice to employ an acoustician for this activity if there is a likelihood of the site works creating noise disturbance, or nuisance.

Figure 4.19
Façade noise monitoring equipment (courtesy ARUP)

Figure 4.20
Free-field noise monitoring equipment (courtesy Parsons Brinckerhoff)

For long-term and possibly unmanned monitoring, extra care should be taken in locating the measurement equipment to minimise both the risk of damage or theft and the influence of other external noise sources, eg fixed building services plant.

Site management need to remain in contact with the person taking measurements to ensure that the measuring equipment will not be affected, or changes will be managed to maintain valid measurements, by changes to the site as the project progresses.

4.6.7   Why is vibration management important?

High vibration levels over a sustained period can cause damage to buildings, while lower vibration levels can cause disturbance to residents. By properly informing local residents of the likelihood that vibration will occur, the less likely they are to complain.

How to avoid vibration problems

The primary aims in the management of vibration on site are to avoid:

☐   causing annoyance and concerns

☐   being (falsely) accused of causing damage

☐   causing damage to nearby structures.

The following six steps will help in addressing each of these aims.

1   Evaluate the potential for vibration and damage

Transmission of vibration is highly dependent on ground conditions and on features in the ground, such as pipe runs. Prediction methods do exist, but they require specialist expertise to implement and rely on detailed information being available on the site, the ground conditions and the plant.

Guidance regarding vibration damage to buildings is contained within BS 7385: Parts 1 (1990) and 2 (1993). Guidance to evaluating human exposure to vibration in buildings is contained within BS 6472-1:2008. See also BS 5228-1:2009.

If it appears that a piling or ground engineering project will generate vibrations putting nearby structures at risk, then a detailed study should be undertaken by specialists. In most other situations it should be sufficient for personnel to review the operations to take place on site and establish the sensitive areas around the site that may need to be monitored.

2   Monitor conditions before works start

Before starting the construction operations, it is important to survey sensitive locations and structures. The survey should include a detailed record of:

☐   existing cracks and their widths

☐   level and plumb survey, including damp-proof course measurements of tilting walls or bulges

☐   other existing damage including loose or broken tiles, pipes, gullies or plaster

Photographic records and installation of measurable devices are helpful to establish alleged or actual damage. In some situations it will be necessary to strengthen vulnerable off-site structures before vibrations start.

Sensitive locations to survey and monitor before and during construction would include (listed in alphabetical order rather than by importance):

☐   aquatic habitats nearby

☐   brittle/ancient underground services including tunnels

☐   buildings in poor condition

☐   historic buildings

☐   hospitals and nursing homes

☐   housing

☐   laboratories

☐   museums

☐   precision machine workshops

☐   schools

☐   sensitive plant or equipment used by local companies.

3   Inform neighbours

Vibration causes anxiety and annoyance to residents mostly because they fear that it will cause damage. It is useful to explain to people that damage only occurs at vibration levels many times greater than those that can be felt from construction plant.

Figure 4.21
Signage
informing public
of noise on site
(courtesy TT2 Ltd)

Informing neighbours of the potential for vibration allows site personnel to learn of any particularly sensitive issues that may be time-dependent and that may be resolved by limiting hours of work.

4   Minimise effects during works

The adoption of BPM to minimise noise and vibration should have identified the best low vibration method for the completion of a construction task. If there are further concerns about the vibration impact of a construction method then they should be revisited at this stage.

The following specific BPM measures should be considered:

☐   can the activity be undertaken using a different methodology that results in lower levels of vibration at the nearby sensitive receptor?

☐   as high frequency vibration causes less damage than low frequency vibration, can the plant be operated in a mode that generates less low frequency vibration (eg vibratory roller, wacker-plates)?

☐   can the plant be isolated from the transfer medium (ie what it's sitting on)? Can plant be placed on a heavy base, which causes less vibration than plant on a lighter base (eg mount plant on the ground rather than on suspended structures)?

5   **Monitor vibration levels during the works**

To be effective, monitoring of vibration levels should be carried out by trained personnel or by external specialists. However, it may be necessary for site personnel to discuss with building occupants where vibration monitoring can be conducted.

When monitoring at properties during operations, the two main rules are:

☐   measure inside rooms when assessing for nuisance

☐   measure on the structure outside when assessing for damage (doorsteps are a good location).

Do not forget that in sensitive structures continued visual monitoring and measurement of crack widths is the best way to determine whether damage is being caused.

6   **Monitor conditions after works are completed**

The same evaluation as undertaken for Step 2 should be carried out and results compared to the precondition surveys.

4.6.8   Good practice checklists

Noise

Change the working method to use equipment or modes of operation that produce less noise. For example:	
☐ in demolition works use hydraulic shears in place of hydraulic impact breakers	
☐ in driving steel sheet piles consider the jacking method (subject to soil conditions, eg cohesive soils), which produce only a fraction of the noise of conventional hammer-driven piling	
☐ when breaking out pavements consider other methods than pneumatic breakers and drills, including chemical splitters or falling weight breakers.	
Reduce the need for noisy assembly practices, eg fabricate off site	
Keep noisy plant as far away as possible from sensitive receptors	
Adopt working hours to restrict noisy activities to certain periods of the day	
Arrange delivery times to suit the area – daytime for residential areas, perhaps night time for commercial inner city areas	
Route construction vehicles to take account of the need to reduce noise and vibration	
Keep haul roads well maintained	
Use mufflers or silencers to reduce noise transmitted along pipes and ducts	
Minimise the drop height into hoppers, lorries or other plant (reducing the drop height by a factor of 10 reduces noise by about 10 dB)	
Consider using rubber linings on tippers in very sensitive site	
Liaise with nature conservation bodies to minimise noise disturbance (disruption) to any sensitive wildlife	

Screens

Where possible, place sources of noise away from sensitive receptors	
Avoid sound traps that amplify noise	
Erect the screen close to the source of noise	
Build the screen from materials with density of 7 kg/m² or higher, with panels stiffened to prevent drumming	
For the most effective results build the screen about 1 m above the highest sight line	
Seal all gaps and openings, including gaps at the bottom of the screen	
Glaze any public observation openings in perimeter hoardings with Perspex (protected with wire mesh or similar) if sensitive receptors are lower than the height of the hoarding	
Consider placing more screens close to sensitive receptors but not parallel to nearby walls	

Vibration

Change the working method to use equipment or modes of operation that produce less vibration, for example: ☐ breaking out concrete, where practicable, should be undertaken using equipment that breaks by bending rather than by percussion ☐ where practicable, rotary drills and bursters actuated by hydraulic or electrical power should be used for excavating hard material.	
Undertake vibration activities as far away as possible from sensitive receptors	
Adopt working hours to restrict high vibration generating activities to certain periods of the day	
Suitable anti-vibration mountings should be fitted where practicable to rotating and/or impacting equipment	
Keep haul roads well maintained	
Consider using rubber linings on tippers in sensitive sites	

4.6.9   Further guidance

General guidance

BRUEL and KJOER (1982) *Noise control: principles and practice*, Naerum, Denmark (ISBN: 8-78735-542-6)

ODPM (2005) Minerals Policy Statement 2 (MPS2): *Controlling and Mitigating the Environmental Effects of Minerals Extraction in England, Annex 2: Noise*, Office of the Deputy Prime Minister, London *

WILLS, A J and CHURCHER, D W (1999) *How much noise do you make? A guide to assessing and managing noise on construction sites*, PR70, CIRIA, London (ISBN: 978-0-86017-870-5)

British Standards

BS 7385-2:1993 *Evaluation and measurement for vibration in buildings. Guide to damage levels from groundborne vibration*

BS 4142:1997 *Method for rating industrial noise affecting mixed residential and industrial areas*

BS 8233:1999 *Sound insulation and noise reduction for buildings. Code of practice*

BS 6472-1:2008 *Guide to evaluation of human exposure to vibration in buildings. Vibration sources other than blasting*

BS 5228-1:2009 *Code of practice for noise and vibration control on construction and open sites. Noise*

BS 5228-2:2009 *Code of practice for noise and vibration control on construction and open sites. Vibration*

*   denotes that a copy of the document is included on the accompanying resource CD

Relevant toolbox talks
(refer to Appendix A4)

Noise and vibration

Archaeology

Be a good neighbour

4.6.10   Legislation

The following table is a brief summary of applicable legislation for this
environmental issue, including requirements and divided by UK region.
Due to frequent legislative developments users should check
<**www.netregs.gov.uk**> when using the table.

Legislation	Key requirements	Direct site requirements	Indirect requirements	Application time planning/during
England				
Environmental Protection Act 1990	Under section 80 local authorities can serve an abatement notice upon the cause of a statutory nuisance to stop work immediately	If an abatement notice is served, ensure work ceases immediately and consult with the local authority	Before construction follow best available techniques and consult with all relevant stakeholders if noise and vibration are likely to be caused by the processes on site	Planning During construction
Control of Pollution Act (CoPA) 1974	A local authority can serve a Section 60 notice if the conditions of the Section 61 consent are breached or if there is no Section 61 in place and excessive noise is being produced	A Section 61 consent can be applied for from the local authority before works begin. This specifies what plant and machinery may be used, the working hours and acceptable noise levels	N/A	Planning During construction
Control of Noise at Work Regulations 2005	Sets noise limits that employers must provide protection to their workers for	The level at which employers must provide hearing protection and hearing protection zones is 85 dB (daily or weekly average exposure) and the level that employers must assess the risk to workers' health at and provide them with information and training is 80 dB. There is an exposure limit value of 87 dB, taking account of any reduction in exposure provided by hearing protection, above which workers must not be exposed	N/A	Planning During construction

Legislation	Key requirements	Direct site requirements	Indirect requirements	Application time planning/during construction/post
The Noise Emissions in the Environment by Equipment for use Outdoors Regulations 2001	The intention of the legislation is to control and monitor noise of equipment for use outdoors. Construction plant and equipment must carry an appropriate label to indicate that it conforms to the levels given in the regulations for that type of machinery	Ensure all construction plant and equipment carries an appropriate label and is conforming to all regulations	N/A	Planning During construction
Construction Plant and Equipment (Harmonisation of Noise Emission Standards) Regulations 1985 and 1988	An EC examination certificate is required before any item of construction plant and equipment may be marketed. Construction plant and equipment must carry an EC mark to indicate that it conforms to the levels given in the regulations for that type of machinery. Failure to comply with, or contravention of, the regulations may result in a fine of up to £2000	Ensure all construction plant and equipment carries the EC mark and is conforming to all regulations	N/A	Planning During construction
Wales				
Environmental Protection Act 1990	Under section 80 local authorities can serve an abatement notice upon the cause of a statutory nuisance to stop work immediately	If an abatement notice is served, ensure work ceases immediately and consult with the local authority	Before construction follow best available techniques and consult with all relevant stakeholders if noise and vibration are likely to be caused by the processes on site	Planning During construction

Legislation	Key requirements	Direct site requirements	Indirect requirements	Application time planning/during construction/post
Control of Pollution Act (CoPA) 1974	A local authority can serve a Section 60 notice if the conditions of the Section 61 consent are breached or if there is no Section 61 in place and excessive noise is being produced	A Section 61 consent can be applied for from the local authority before works begin. This specifies what plant and machinery may be used, the working hours and acceptable noise levels	N/A	Planning

During construction |
| Control of Noise at Work Regulations 2005 | Sets noise limits at which employers must provide protection to their workers the level at which employers must assess the risk to workers' health and provide them with information and training is 80 dB | The level at which employers must provide hearing protection and hearing protection zones is now 85 dB (daily or weekly average exposure) and the level at which employers must assess the risk to workers' health and provide them with information and training is now 80 dB. There is also an exposure limit value of 87 decibels, taking account of any reduction in exposure provided by hearing protection, above which workers must not be exposed | N/A | Planning

During construction |
| Construction Plant and Equipment (Harmonisation of Noise Emission Standards) Regulations 1985 and 1988 | An EC examination certificate is required before any item of construction plant and equipment may be marketed. Construction plant and equipment must carry an EC mark to indicate that it conforms to the levels given in the regulations for that type of machinery. Failure to comply with, or contravention of, the regulations may result in a fine of up to £2000 | Ensure all construction plant and equipment carries the EC mark and is conforming to all regulations | N/A | Planning

During construction |

Legislation	Key requirements	Direct site requirements	Indirect requirements	Application time planning/during construction/post
Scotland				
Control of Pollution Act (CoPA) 1974	A local authority can serve a Section 60 notice if the conditions of the Section 61 consent are breached or if there is no Section 61 in place and excessive noise is being produced	A Section 61 consent can be applied for from the local authority before works begin. This specifies what plant and machinery may be used, the working hours and acceptable noise levels	N/A	Planning During construction
Control of Noise at Work Regulations 2005	Sets noise limits at which employers must provide protection to their workers the level at which employers must assess the risk to workers' health and provide them with information and training is 80 dB	The level at which employers must provide hearing protection and hearing protection zones is now 85 dB (daily or weekly average exposure) and the level at which employers must assess the risk to workers' health and provide them with information and training is now 80 dB. There is also an exposure limit value of 87 dB, taking account of any reduction in exposure provided by hearing protection, above which workers must not be exposed	N/A	Planning During construction

Legislation	Key requirements	Direct site requirements	Indirect requirements	Application time planning/during construction/post
Construction Plant and Equipment (Harmonisation of Noise Emission Standards) Regulations 1985 and 1988	An EC examination certificate is required before any item of construction plant and equipment may be marketed. Construction plant and equipment must carry an EC mark to indicate that it conforms to the levels given in the regulations for that type of machinery. Failure to comply with, or contravention of, the regulations may result in a fine of up to £2000	Ensure all construction plant and equipment carries the EC mark and is conforming to all regulations	N/A	Planning During construction
Northern Ireland				
The Pollution Control and Local Government (NI) Order 1978	Complaints can be made against a noise or vibration source under Article 39. Magistrates can then serve an abatement notice upon the cause of a statutory nuisance to stop work immediately	If an abatement notice is served, ensure work ceases immediately and consult with the local authority	Before construction follow best available techniques and consult with all relevant stakeholders if noise and vibration are likely to be caused by the processes on site	Planning During construction

Legislation	Key requirements	Direct site requirements	Indirect requirements	Application time planning/during construction/post
The Control of Noise at Work Regulations (Northern Ireland) 2006	Sets noise limits at which employers must provide protection to their workers the level at which employers must assess the risk to workers' health and provide them with information and training is 80 dB	The level at which employers must provide hearing protection and hearing protection zones is now 85 dB (daily or weekly average exposure) and the level at which employers must assess the risk to workers' health and provide them with information and training is now 80 dB. There is also an exposure limit value of 87 dB, taking account of any reduction in exposure provided by hearing protection, above which workers must not be exposed	N/A	Planning During construction
The Construction Plant and Equipment (Harmonisation of Noise Emission Standards) (Extension to Northern Ireland) Regulations 1992	An EC examination certificate is required before any item of construction plant and equipment may be marketed. Construction plant and equipment must carry an EC mark to indicate that it conforms to the levels given in the regulations for that type of machinery. Failure to comply with, or contravention of, the regulations may result in a fine of up to £2000	Ensure all construction plant and equipment carries the EC mark and is conforming to all regulations	N/A	Planning During construction

Legislation	Key requirements	Direct site requirements	Indirect requirements	Application time planning/during construction/post
Public Health (Ireland) Act 1878	Sets out rules on statutory nuisance, including noise, which could lead to the local council or the DoE issuing an abatement notice	If an abatement notice is served, ensure work ceases immediately and consult with the local authority	Before construction follow best available techniques and consult with all relevant stakeholders if dust emissions or odours are likely to be caused by the processes on site	Planning During construction

4.7   Traffic, travel management and vehicle use

4.7.1   Why management of traffic and vehicle use is important

There are many good reasons to manage traffic coming to site, on site and leaving it. Traffic on roads around the site can cause nuisance through noise, exhaust emissions, dust, congestion and mud.

On-site traffic generates dust and noise and carries risks of damaging materials and causing pollution incidents (eg vehicles damaging oil containers causing ground pollution). Site traffic also forms part of a site's carbon footprint and natural resource use (eg fuel), which can be effectively reduced through good planning.

A good traffic management plan (TMP) covers all forms of transport; road vehicles, pedestrians, bicycles and disabled access.

Emissions

There are two further issues to consider in respect to transport to and from and on site:

☐   effect on local and national air quality
☐   carbon dioxide emissions.

From a site management perspective these should offer further encouragement for reducing vehicle movements associated with the site.

In England there are consultation processes underway to set binding reduction targets for on-site CO_2 generation. For further information see Strategic Forum and Carbon Trust who are defining the methodology on behalf of the Strategy for Sustainable Construction's target of 15 per cent reduction in carbon emissions from construction processes and associated transport compared to 2008 levels.

Also, clients, especially in the public sector, are requiring the production of carbon footprints for projects, leading to reduction targets.

4.7.2   Traffic management plan

A TMP should enable operatives to manage all these risks efficiently and effectively. It should be clearly written and presented, and well communicated to all site staff, subcontractors and suppliers. It is good practice to regularly review the TMP and to make sure that significant changes to the plan are appropriately communicated.

The TMP should include both off-site (ie travel to and from site, deliveries etc) and on-site (plant and car movements on site) traffic management requirements.

For details on what information should be included in a site TMP refer to the checklist at the end of this section.

Figure 4.22
Vehicle leaving site (courtesy Bovis Lend Lease)

On-site traffic

Plan to reduce nuisance, potential impacts to materials, and polluting substances by:

- □ planning on-site roads as one-way systems
- □ including turning circles
- □ controlling access onto and off the site

- adopting and enforcing speed limits
- preparing roads to prevent dust
- ensuring roads avoid fuel and material storage areas
- ensuring delivery and waste removal vehicles are sheeted to prevent dust or material being blown off
- communicating to drivers the need to comply with rules and to maintain vehicles, and the consequences if these requirements are not applied.

Off-site traffic

Plan the timing of deliveries to avoid vehicles waiting. Where several deliveries are likely to take place over a short period, designate queuing areas away from sensitive areas, in liaison with the local authority if on public roads. In urban areas it may be best to allocate a waiting area some distance from site and then call in deliveries when access to the site is clear.

Site worker traffic

Site personnel should not be permitted to park vehicles around the site boundary as this will cause a nuisance to local residents and disruption to deliveries. Arrange designated parking areas when there is appropriate space to do so on larger projects. On more confined sites this may not be possible, so workers should be encouraged to vehicle share, or arrangements should be made for a minibus to collect them from local train or bus stations. Local employees should be encouraged to walk or cycle (ensure that facilities such as secure areas to store bikes during the working day are made available) and showers.

4.7.3   Reducing nuisance and congestion around site

It is a good idea to plan traffic movements around a site in consultation with the local authorities and police. It may even be a planning or legal requirement or form part of a Section 61 agreement with a local authority. This will help to identify both important times to avoid deliveries (eg during school runs) and appropriate delivery routes.

The use of public roads for site access may be restricted. Such restrictions may include:

- weight and width controls

- [ ] parking controls
- [ ] low-headroom access routes
- [ ] accessibility.

Figure 4.23
*Signage for vehicle routes
(courtesy Bovis Lend Lease)*

Wherever possible, arrange the access so that all vehicles enter and exit the site in a forward direction.

Materials management plans can help reduce the number of deliveries needed and make sure that they arrive at the right time of day. Details of site access routes and delivery times can be included with orders placed with suppliers on a clear map with written instructions.

Encouraging site staff to car-share or use public transport, and/or providing communal transport can further reduce traffic to and from site. Using alternative site transport, such as bicycles, will help reduce dust, emissions and site hazards.

Mud and debris from roads should be cleared regularly and it may be appropriate to install wheel washing facilities.

Case study 4.7
Liaison undertaken with the distribution
warehouses (courtesy Balfour Beatty)

The project has been in regular contact with Asda, Argos and Amazon – in respect to their shift patterns and how by changing the projects' planned road closure times disruption to their operations can be minimised. Also, regular face to face meetings are held to discuss upcoming works and any potential impacts they may cause.

The project public liaison officer has had particularly close dealings with Asda, especially with the distribution manager, who has attended and presented at the respective project supply chain conference and project progress update.

The presentation was from a stakeholder's point of view, which complimentary about the communications between the company and project and how a positive relationship has built up during the course of the works.

When the project required a special delivery of large reinforced concrete beams Asda allowed the project to use their car park, which prevented the need to close other roads in the area to allow delivery. Asda have attended the project and were taken on a site visit to view the works. A positive working relationship has established a two-way street with mutual interests at heart.

4.7.4   Good practice checklists

 Traffic management plan

Identify sensitive areas (eg schools and homes)	
Plan on-site routes, one way systems and turning circles	
Use speed limits	
Prepare on-site roads to prevent dust	
Be aware of road restrictions either through road works, narrow roads and bridges with height and/or weight restrictions	
Choose suitable materials for use on access roads – to avoid mud and dust on roads	
Take into account other developments whose activities could affect the project	
Identify suitable locations for parking facilities for private cars and plant	
Ensure there are designated walkways on and around site	
Ensure there are designated vehicular routes on site with speed restrictions	
Locate site entrance and exit so they are not off minor roads	
Gain permission for road closure from the highways division of local authority in smaller scale projects (Highways Agency for larger projects)	
Ensure road closures are carried out by a competent person	
Develop a map showing delivery drivers' routes to site from trunk roads	
Schedule site deliveries outside times of peak traffic volume	
Have designated personnel on site to receive deliveries, direct vehicles on and off site, and act as banksman	
Project vehicles should have a badges on their windscreens displaying contact details for the project if they are found to be parked inappropriately	
Offer alternative modes of transport for personnel to site, eg use of minibuses, car sharing or bicycles	
Identify alternative delivery streams, eg canals and railway if feasible	
Monitor vehicle movements to reduce the likelihood of queuing or causing congestion in and around the local area	

Parking

Designate an area on site for site personnel parking	
Prevent delivery vehicles from queuing outside the site boundary	
Make delivery drivers aware of traffic restrictions on and around the site	

Plant and vehicles

Use a wheel wash for vehicles leaving the site to prevent mud being spread on surrounding roads	
Prohibit vehicle washing outside of any designated area on site	
Use mechanical road sweepers and surface flushing apparatus to clean hard standing and remove any mud or debris deposited by site vehicles on roads, footpaths, gullies or drains near to the site	
Ensure that exhausts do not discharge directly at the ground	
Use retractable sheeted covers to protect wind-blown material	
Ensure all plant and vehicles are in good working order	
Reverse sirens – consider lorries with "white noise" alarms to minimise the effects of noise on local residents	
Should emergency maintenance need to be carried out on site, ensure it is in a designated area away from sensitive receptors and that a spill kit is close to hand	

Delivery schedule

All deliveries to site should keep to their allocated time slot. Failure to do so could mean they are turned away	
No deliveries should be accepted on site without contractor personnel to unload them or direct the vehicle	
No materials or rubbish are to be left in the unloading area	
Washout should occur only in designated areas	
All vehicle delivery drivers should wear PPE once inside the delivery area	
Ensure contractors are aware that incorrectly loaded vehicles will not be offloaded	

Site rules for drivers

Access to and from the site will be only via the main entrance gates	
On leaving the site, vehicles are to follow the directions previously given	
All engines to be switched off while waiting to unload	
No parking in residential streets surrounding the site	
All drivers should be asked to proceed with caution particularly at peak school times in the vicinity of local schools	
Drivers should adhere to the site speed limit	
All vehicles entering the site should stop and report to the gateman who will direct them to the required place of loading/unloading	
Avoid the need to reverse where possible, otherwise a competent banksman should be present	
Drivers are asked to park in the designated area and wear appropriate PPE (safety helmet, boots and hi-viz jackets) while away from their vehicles	
All loaded vehicles leaving site should be sheeted – this should be done using a mechanism before entering the wheel wash	
All vehicles should pass through the wheel wash facility and be inspected by the gateman to ensure they are clean before leaving site	
All loaded vehicles leaving site should take the correct documentation with them. Ensure relevant copies of documentation, together with a copy of the weighbridge ticket, are handed to the gateman on return to site	

4.7.5   Further guidance

> **Relevant toolbox talks (refer to Appendix A4)**
>
> Dust and air quality
>
> Noise and vibration
>
> Oil/diesel storage
>
> Washing down plant and machinery
>
> Be a good neighbour

4.7.6   Legislation

The following table is a brief summary of applicable legislation to traffic, travel management and vehicle use, including requirements and divided by UK region. Due to frequent legislative developments users should check <**www.netregs.gov.uk**> when using the table.

Legislation	Key requirements	Direct site requirements	Indirect requirements	Application time *planning/during construction/post*
England				
Highways Act 1990	Ensures, as far as is reasonably practicable, that the highway is kept in a clear and unobstructed condition for the highway user. Anyone contravening the Highways Act is advised accordingly that any obstruction must be removed. Action may on occasion result in legal proceedings against the person contravening the Act	Ensure all construction activities that involve blocking or part obstructing a highway are agreed in advance with the local authority	N/A	Planning During construction
New Roads and Street Works Act (NRSWA) 1991	The local authority has a duty to ensure all traffic management and re-instatements are carried out effectively and efficiently to keep disruption to the highway user to a minimum The council has some powers regarding the timing of street works and the restriction of such works within 12 months of the completion of substantial road works	Ensure all construction activities that involve blocking or part obstructing a highway are agreed in advance with the local authority	N/A	Planning During construction

Legislation	Key requirements	Direct site requirements	Indirect requirements	Application time planning/during construction/post
Wales				
Highways Act 1990	Ensures, as far as is reasonably practicable, that the highway is kept in a clear and unobstructed condition for the highway user. Anyone contravening the Highways Act is advised accordingly that any obstruction must be removed. Occasionally, action may result in legal proceedings against the person contravening the Act	Ensure all construction activities that involve blocking or part obstructing a highway are agreed in advance with the local authority	N/A	Planning During construction
New Roads and Street Works Act (NRSWA) 1991	The local authority has a duty to ensure all traffic management and re-instatements are carried out effectively and efficiently to keep disruption to the highway user to a minimum The council has some powers regarding the timing of street works and the restriction of such works within 12 months of the completion of substantial road works Further legislation has been imposed by the National Assembly for Wales	Ensure all construction activities that involve blocking or part obstructing a highway are agreed in advance with the local authority	N/A	Planning During construction

Legislation	Key requirements	Direct site requirements	Indirect requirements	Application time planning/during construction/post
Scotland				
Roads (Scotland) Act 1984	Ensures, as far as is reasonably practicable, that the highway is kept in a clear and unobstructed condition for the highway user. Anyone contravening the Act is advised accordingly that any obstruction must be removed. Occasionally action may result in legal proceedings against the person contravening the Act	Ensure all construction activities that involve blocking or part obstructing a highway are agreed in advance with the local authority	N/A	Planning During construction
New Roads and Street Works Act (NRSWA) 1991	The local authority has a duty to ensure all traffic management and re-instatements are carried out effectively and efficiently to keep disruption to the highway user to a minimum The council has some powers regarding the timing of street works and the restriction of such works within 12 months of the completion of substantial road works Further legislation has been imposed by the Scottish Executive	Ensure all construction activities that involve blocking or part obstructing a highway are agreed in advance with the local authority	N/A	Planning During construction

Legislation	Key requirements	Direct site requirements	Indirect requirements	Application time planning/during construction/post
Northern Ireland				
The Street Works (Northern Ireland) Order 1995	A Street Works Licence is required by any person or organisation who wishes to place or retain apparatus in a street, and inspect, maintain, adjust, repair, alter or renew the apparatus, change its position or remove it after, unless the person or organisation has a statutory right to do so. Any person who carries out such works without a Street Works Licence or a statutory right is committing an offence and liable on summary conviction to a fine	Ensure all construction activities that involve blocking or part obstructing a highway are agreed in advance with the local authority and licences are obtained where necessary	N/A	Planning During construction

4.8   Waste

4.8.1   Introduction

Legally, waste is defined as something the owner "discards or intends to discard or intends or is required to discard." This can include materials that other people want, or for which they can find a beneficial use.

In England and Wales the construction and demolition industry is responsible for generating up to 110 million tonnes of waste per year and approximately 25 million tonnes of this total is sent to landfill. The total amount of waste generated equates to about one third of all waste produced in a year in England and Wales, and makes up around half of all controlled waste in Scotland. The industry is the third largest producer of hazardous waste.

Waste not only significantly affects the environment, but handling waste inefficiently will cost time, money and effort. For example, by not segregating waste initially, inert material may have to be disposed of as active or hazardous waste, depending on which waste it is mixed with. Often people think that waste costs are related only to its disposal. In fact, the true cost of waste is eight to 10 times the disposal cost and includes:

☐   purchase price of materials that are being wasted

☐   cost of storage, transport and disposal of excess materials/waste

☐   cost of the time spent managing and handling the waste

☐   loss of income from not reusing waste materials.

4.8.2   Waste impacts

The environmental impacts of waste are many and wide ranging, but can be sub-divided into the following:

Direct impacts

☐   emissions – any processing of waste before disposal (on or off site) requires energy, so contributes to emissions to atmosphere

☐   energy emissions from transport – each load of waste removed from site is responsible for transport emissions to the atmosphere

☐   landfill emissions – as waste undergoes chemical, physical and biological change in landfill it releases emissions to the atmosphere, such as CO_2 and methane, that then affects air quality and contributes to emissions into the atmosphere of greenhouse gases

☐ land use – disposal to landfill requires the use and pollution of land, which takes away a commodity that could be used for more beneficial purposes, or simply left for ecological value.

Indirect impacts

☐ impacts of raw material use and energy consumption in production of product, material, packaging etc before becoming a waste

☐ recycling uses energy, produces emission pollutions and generates waste

☐ landfill as polluted land requires extensive clean up before it can be reused

☐ pollution in foreign countries through export of wastes, particularly electronic and/or hazardous wastes, for processing and disposal

☐ energy use and emissions as a consequence of transport, processing and disposal of waste following transfer of waste to new holder.

The effects of waste at regional, national and international levels are wide ranging and collectively there is a major impact on the environment. Waste is considered as one of the most important environmental issues to manage properly.

There are two principles of effectively managing waste:

1 Resource efficiency – ensuring the efficient use of resources to reduce the generation of waste in the first instance.

2 Effective waste management – divert remaining waste from landfill (reuse, recycle etc).

These principles are acted upon through several mechanisms in the UK construction industry, from European Directives through to National Legislation.

Legislation as it applies to a construction site can be summarised as having two principle aims in the industry: to ensure the disposal of waste is regulated (and traceable) and to ensure that the cost of waste disposal is borne by the waste producer, in-line with the polluter pays principle (PPP).

To meet the wider aims of reducing the amount of waste produced and diverting waste from landfill there are many strategies in place, which are highlighted in the following section.

4.8.3   Definition of different types of waste

The European Waste Catalogue (EWC) can be used to identify waste and assigns a six digit code to it, which helps to determine how waste can be disposed. Under the Duty of Care Regulations these six digit codes are required to be written on waste transfer notes. In England the List of Wastes (England) Regulations 2005, and in Wales the List of Waste (Wales) Regulations transpose the requirements of the EWC into national regulation. For the purposes of landfill disposal, wastes can be subdivided into the following:

☐   inert waste covers materials that do not undergo significant physical, chemical or biological reactions or cause environmental pollution or harm to human health or endanger the quality of any surface water or groundwater when deposited in a landfill under normal conditions. These include rocks, ceramics, concrete, masonry, and brick rubble

☐   active/non-hazardous wastes are wastes that do not feature on the list of hazardous waste in the EWC 2002, but are not inert wastes. These include timber and bitumen (depending on tar content)

☐   hazardous wastes possessing one or more of the 14 hazardous properties in the Hazardous Waste Directive, including those that are deemed to be dangerous to life and/or damaging to the environment. Hazardous wastes may be corrosive, reactive, explosive, oxidising, carcinogenic or flammable. Examples include asbestos, acids, alkaline solutions, oily sludges, waste oils and wood preservatives:

  ☐   hazardous wastes are identified in the List of Waste Regulations 2005

  ☐   controls over hazardous wastes are defined in the Hazardous Wastes (England and Wales) Regulations 2005 (as amended in 2009) in England only and the Special Waste Regulations 1996 (as amended) in Scotland and in Northern Ireland the Hazardous Waste Regulations (Northern Ireland) 2005.

4.8.4   Waste management initiatives

Strategy for Sustainable Construction 2008

A joint government and industry document setting targets and actions for the construction industry. The overarching waste target is that by 2012, a 50 per cent reduction of construction, demolition and excavation (CD&E) waste to landfill compared to 2008.

Halving waste to landfill

A voluntary UK-wide sector goal established by WRAP, where organisations commit to playing their part in helping the sector halve the amount of waste going to landfill by 2012 in response to the targets set in the Sustainable Construction Strategy. Almost 400 companies had signed up to this target by 2010 from all parts of the supply chain including, clients, contractors, designers, suppliers/manufacturers and waste management contractors.

National strategies

Each of the UK regions have developed and published there own strategies for waste management by setting targets and developing process to reduce the amount of waste produced.

DEFRA (2007) *Waste Strategy for England*, Department of Environment, Food and Rural Affairs, London
Go to: <www.defra.gov.uk>

THE SCOTTISH GOVERNMENT (2010) *Scotland's Zero Waste Plan*, The Scottish Government, Edinburgh
Go to: <www.scotland.gov.uk>

WELSH ASSEMBLY GOVERNMENT (2009) *Wales Waste Strategy 2009–2050: Towards zero waste*, Welsh Assembley Government, Cardiff
Go to: <www.wales.gov.uk>

NIEA (2006) *The Northern Ireland Waste Management Strategy 2006–2020*, Northern Ireland Environment Agency, Belfast
Go to: <www.ni-environment.gov.uk>

Case study 4.8
Woolwich barracks regeneration
(courtesy Bovis Lend Lease)

Bovis Lend Lease and Debut Services employed the WRAP Regeneration guide methods to inform and influence the feasibility, planning and delivery stages of work related to the regeneration of Woolwich barracks in the east end of London. This was part of the SLAM (single living accommodation modernisation) project.

The main outcomes were:

☐ overall cost savings of between £26 250 (£7.50/tonne) and £42 000 (£12.00/tonne) were achieved by retaining and reprocessing 3500 of the 12 000 tonnes of demolition arisings – to be used as recycled aggregate instead of hauling the material off site and importing aggregates. This was subject to compatibility with the contract specifications

☐ a demolition recovery index (DRI) of 95 per cent was set as the target for recovering material from site

☐ the retained material KPI was 29 per cent, indicating that although there was a limited demand for aggregates within the footprint of the modular build (3500 tonnes) there was still a significant opportunity to improve the sustainability of the project in terms of the approach to materials resource efficiency

☐ the target for recycled content of bulk materials in the new build was 100 per cent

☐ analysing recycled content levels using WRAP's net waste tool on the modular build design determined a current standard project performance of 16 per cent recycled content by value. Through closer inspection of the specification this could be improved to a good practice (quick win) level of 20 per cent and a potential to achieve a best practice level of 23 per cent

☐ besides a carbon reduction, other environmental benefits were identified in relation to 350 reduced vehicle trips and their associated nuisance (noise, vibration and dust), and the result of retaining demolition arisings on-site for reprocessing

☐ the carbon footprint of the development was reduced by about 11 tonnes through a reduction of the number of vehicle movements

☐ the use of recovered materials would reduce the extraction of virgin aggregate materials, improving the longevity and sustainability of this industry moving into the future.

4.8.5   The waste hierarchy

Waste management priorities and practical actions that can be undertaken on site should follow the principles of the waste hierarchy, which is now included in the Waste Framework Directive (see Figure 4.24).

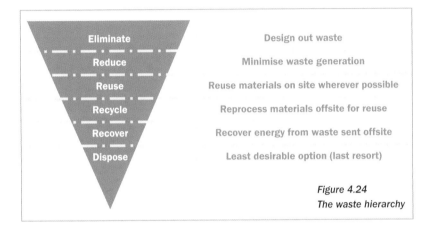

Eliminate	Design out waste
Reduce	Minimise waste generation
Reuse	Reuse materials on site wherever possible
Recycle	Reprocess materials offsite for reuse
Recover	Recover energy from waste sent offsite
Dispose	Least desirable option (last resort)

Figure 4.24
The waste hierarchy

4.8.6   Waste management duty of care

There is a duty of care to ensure that waste is dealt with appropriately. The person on site with responsibility for waste management must be able to describe both the waste kept on site and the waste transported off site. Disposal of waste from site must only be carried out by a registered waste carrier who should be able to provide a colour copy of their waste carriers' licence. Details of the license can be checked with the environmental regulator. The waste should only go to a site that is either licensed or exempt as appropriate.

4.8.7   The Landfill Directive

The Landfill Directive seeks to bring about a change in the way waste is disposed. Its overall aim is:

"to prevent or reduce as far as possible negative effects on the environment, in particular the pollution of surface water, groundwater, soil and air, and on the global environment, including the greenhouse effect, as well as any resulting risk to human health, from the landfilling of waste, during the whole life cycle of the landfill".

The Directive has provisions covering location of landfills, and technical and engineering requirements for aspects such as water control and leachate management, protection of soil and water and methane emissions control.

The directive sets demanding targets to reduce the amount of biodegradable municipal landfilled waste.

4.8.8   Environmental Permitting Regulations

The Environmental Permitting (England and Wales) Regulations (as amended) 2010 require "waste operations" to hold an environmental permit (subject to certain exemptions). Waste operations are defined by reference to the Waste Framework Directive and mean any recovery (including storage pending recycling/reclamation etc) or disposal of waste that requires an environmental permit, unless the waste operation is specifically exempt or excluded under the regulations.

In Northern Ireland the Waste Management Licensing Regulations (Northern Ireland) 2003 apply. Waste operations will be authorised by a waste management licence, an exemption from waste management licensing or a Pollution Prevention & Control (PPC) permit, depending on the nature of the waste management activity.

It is important to identify whether an environmental permit is required for operations carried out on or off site.

4.8.9   Waste management on site

To effectively manage waste on site, a standard approach should be adopted as follows:

1   Planning.
2   Managing.
3   Monitoring and reporting.

These collectively combine good practice techniques and legislation. This approach is defined in the Site Waste Managements Plan (England) Regulations 2008 and is reflected in this section of the guide.

Figure 4.25 outlines the activities to apply waste management on site. The following section explains this process in more detail:

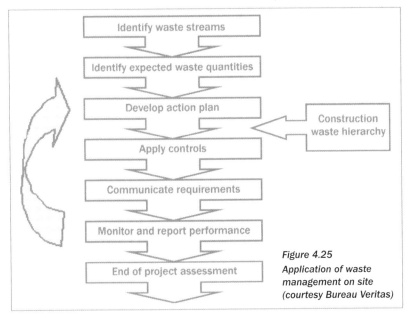

Figure 4.25

Application of waste management on site (courtesy Bureau Veritas)

1 Planning

Development of a SWMP is a legal requirement in England for all construction projects over £300 000 (excl. VAT) in project value. In other UK regions the legal requirements for England should be considered as a good practice approach. Also, there is a large quantity of available good practice guidance and tools (eg SWMP templates) available to the industry. See <**www.wrap.org.uk/construction/index.html**>, <**www.environment-agency.gov.uk**>, or <**www.netregs.gov.uk**>.

Waste management planning requires the involvement of the majority of the project team, including the client, contractors, designers and personnel not based on site. It is necessary to identify one site-based employee from the main/principal contractor to be responsible for the development and implementation of the SWMP. This individual should have sufficient knowledge and experience of the project processes and enough influence within the project team to ensure that the SWMP is effective.

Client and designers role in planning SWMP

The client should be involved in the planning stage. However, the most beneficial waste reduction opportunities should be identified by members of the design team that may include engineers, architects and quantity surveyors. This will ensure that waste reduction decisions and actions are achievable and agreed by all who are involved in the project delivery. Many of the most effective methods to reduce waste are achieved through design and specifications on projects. It is a requirement of the SWMP, in England, that the client and principle contractor sign a joint declaration of commitment to the SWMP as developed.

Earthworks planning

For earthworks it is worth considering the Contaminated Land: Applications in Real Environments (CL:AIRE) code of practice. This document sets out auditable good practice methodology that can be applied for assessing whether or not materials are classified as waste and for determining when treated waste can cease to be waste for a particular use. This will help to identify whether or not an environmental permit may be required.

2 Managing waste

Identify waste streams

Undertake a desktop review of the project plans, programme, design etc, and identify each type of waste that is expected to be produced, including identifying wastes that are inactive, active and hazardous. Record the expected wastes in the SWMP.

For each type of waste identified, estimate the quantities of waste that are expected to be generated and the expected cost of traditional disposal. This estimation should be based on previous experience, or industry averages. WRAP's net waste tool can be used to forecast arisings as well as assess recycled content.

By identifying potential waste streams (types and quantities) that could arise during the various stages of a construction project, there is a greater likelihood that these can be effectively managed and diverted from landfill.

For each waste stream identified consideration needs to be given as to how the waste will be disposed of, eg timber off-cuts, general active waste skip, landfill.

The information gathered on waste streams and disposal routes to estimate the expected costs for waste disposal. This is the cost expected to pay for wastes identified if no improvements are made to the disposal options eg material x skip hire x transfer fees x disposal cost x no. of skips = £xxx.

Develop waste action plan

Using the principles of the waste hierarchy a plan should be developed for each waste stream identified. Opportunities for each stage of the hierarchy should be considered and the most suitable (practical, financial, technical) option selected. This plan should demonstrate both reductions in overall waste expected to be generated and the reductions in waste to be sent to landfill.

To develop suitable actions it is important that the client and architect and/or designers are involved in the process. In some contracts this may require subcontractors input. Examples include:

☐ developing standardised sizes or pre-cut materials to reduce off cuts (eg timber)

☐ negotiating take-back schemes with suppliers

☐ providing storage areas for materials to be reused on site

☐ specifying/negotiating reduction in the amount of packaging used by suppliers, or packaging return schemes

☐ specifying pre-cast units, (eg concrete panels rather than on-site pours).

Waste management should start with resource efficiency by using the raw materials procured more wisely. To manage wastes effectively, focus on ways to prevent materials becoming waste (see Section 4.5).

Each waste stream in the action plan should have a corresponding action (some may require more than one action) to reduce waste. These can be used to monitor progress in reducing waste.

Record the waste action plan within the SWMP document for the site.

The SWMP should include details of disposal methods for waste on the project, for instance waste carriers and waste disposal facilities. At the time of planning it is important to take into account the availability of facilities in the area of the site.

4   Environmental issues

At this stage ensure to obtain copies of environmental permits for each of the waste streams identified (including appropriate waste management licenses if working in Northern Ireland or Scotland).

During construction if waste material is to be stored on site before collection and treatment then an environmental permit or exemption could be required, resulting in extra costs to the project. An exemption may be required for storing, crushing or reusing waste. In England and Wales ensure compliance with the Environmental Permitting Regulations (England & Wales) 2010 as amended, and seek guidance from regulators (see <**www.netregs.gov.uk**>)

Case study 4.9
Waste management during contaminated land remediation (courtesy Morrison Construction)

One of the largest tyre dumps in Europe was remediated by Morrison Construction using tyre stabilisation and capping techniques. The first stage involved re-profiling the remaining tyres into a regular shape and covering them. The second stage involved the construction of a specifically designed cover, which comprised a layer of geogrid membrane, a layer of inert waste shale from a local source and completed with a layer of local limestone.

Details of materials reused on the project to reduce the amount of waste generated included:

☐   use of 19 000 tonnes of waste shale and limestone dust in the engineering cap, which would have gone to landfill. This material was acquired through the procurement system and resulted in a landfill tax saving of £455 000, more than the actual project value

☐   concrete slabs that were already present on site were used as temporary security fencing/road blocks during the scheme and then made into a permanent fence on project completion

☐   mature trees taken down to make way for the engineering cap were made into log sections and stored on site. On completion of the cap were then redistributed around the site in log piles to provide new habitat for hibernating mammals or reptiles and ground nesting birds

☐   limestone blocks already in situ were used for habitat provision. These latter two initiatives were not part of the original design, but provided added value to the scheme by encouraging new habitat to flourish on the site, which had previously been an eyesore and a drain on local resources.

Once the waste has been suitably treated on site in accordance with the waste exemption and fulfils the WRAP quality protocol, it is no longer classed as waste and can be used for its defined purpose on site.

The client should be involved in the planning stage, including architects and designers as applicable, and it is a requirement of the Site Waste Management Plans Regulations 2008 that the client and principle contractor sign a joint declaration of commitment to the SWMP developed.

Ensure that the SWMP is readily available on site throughout the lifetime of the project.

Apply controls

Having defined the SWMP and action plan, apply controls on site to ensure that the plans are achieved: this starts with defining facilities.

Define facilities on site

Ensure that sufficient space is allocated on site for the waste expected to generate. This should include the transfer of waste from remote locations to a central waste area. Clearly mark these areas on site plans for communication purposes.

When waste is being stored on site it is important that the storage areas have clear signage to ensure different wastes are stored in the correct place. EnCams, the Institution of Civil Engineers (ICE) and UKCG have developed standardised waste signage. Further details can be found at <**www.wasteawareconstruction.org**> where a poster creator is available to make customised versions (see Figures 4.26 and 4.27).

Before stockpiling wastes on site for reuse or recycling, identify where the material is going to be used. If there is no space on site to segregate wastes for reuse or recycling, consider off site recycling by using a waste management subcontractor that has the necessary facilities. Consider the use of reused and recycled materials on site. To find sources of such materials talk to local demolition contractors and local authority recycling officers.

Whatever storage provided it should be:

☐ clearly marked, eg use wasteaware signs

☐ enclosed to prevent waste escaping, eg blown by wind

☐ segregated by type where possible

☐ suitable for that waste type, ie able to contain waste and prevent escape, including leaking of liquids.

In addition:

☐ hazardous wastes must not be mixed

☐ hazardous wastes must be stored in suitable containment.

If it is intended to use a material recovery facility (MRF) to sort and recycle waste, it will be necessary to discuss the on site facility requirements with the contractor to ensure that the best results are achieved. This will include establishing exactly what can be placed in a general waste skip without contaminating the waste and preventing it being recovered and recycled.

Figure 4.26
Segregated skips
(courtesy Kier)

Figure 4.27
Skip on site
(courtesy Kier)

Communicate

As each site and each site's SWMP will have different requirements for waste management, it is important that these requirements are communicated to relevant parties (ie site personnel and subcontractors).

All persons working on site should be made aware of the waste management requirements at induction as a minimum. Under the Site Waste Management Plans (England) Regulations 2008, the principal contractor must make the SWMP available to all contractors carrying out work on their behalf, and ensure that these contractors know where the SWMP is kept on site.

Ensure that the SWMP is readily available on site for all to use and for regulator review if required (England only).

Induct

Ensure that the site specific requirements for waste as defined in the SWMP (including relevant action plans) are included in the site induction, and provided to all who work on site. This does not need to be the full details of the plan, but just those areas relevant to their activities.

Case study 4.10
Material reuse during a flood defence scheme
(courtesy Morrison Construction)

This project was to develop a flood defence scheme to protect a town centre including residential properties, local transportation and amenity services (bus depots and supermarkets) from flooding. Work comprised raising the existing flood defence wall, replacing and upgrading the existing footpath, creating new access paths, roads and flood storage areas.

During the project the materials were reused as follows:

☐ temporary flood defence was required during the building of the wall. Normally this would entail using sand bags, however these have only limited use once they are wet and would probably be disposed of. Instead of this option, bags of aggregate were used. These provided adequate flood defence until the main wall was constructed. The aggregate was then used as sub base for footpath construction

☐ concrete from demolition of existing structures was recycled by crushing using a muncher then used as general fill material. For example the concrete was used on haul roads and when these were removed it was used as a capping layer for the new footpaths

☐ trees removed as part of construction were shredded and reused as mulch, which was used for landscaping and promoting the growth of new habitats

☐ replacement of existing walls with re-profiled slope and concrete retaining wall and composite sheet pile retaining wall and concrete L wall section

☐ after waste acceptance criteria (WAC) testing non hazardous material excavated from behind the existing flood defence wall to help the construction of the new wall was reused as backfill for the same area. This eliminated the need to import other material onto site saving time and money

☐ in addition to the non-hazardous material, approximately 50 tonnes of heavily contaminated material was located in the excavation behind the existing flood wall. Instead of costly disposal at hazardous landfill sites over 50 miles away, it was recycled locally at a soil washing facility, some 15 miles from the site. It is estimated that this saved approximately £3000–£4000 mainly in transportation costs and landfill entrance fees

☐ imported gravel material that was used to create the piling platform was reused on site as backfill material behind new flood defence wall.

3 Monitoring and reporting performance

Updating the SWMP

It is a requirement of the Site Waste Management Plans (England) Regulations 2008, and considered good practice, that the site SWMP must be updated each time waste is removed from site. Updates will use the waste transfer/consignment notes information, and following this procedure provides a useful check that the transfer notes are being completed correctly.

A thorough review of the SWMP should be carried out monthly, to assess performance against the waste action plan and targets. The review should include calculating the costs of waste treatment and disposal.

The site manager should allocate responsibility to a nominated individual to carry out waste audits/inspections at regular intervals to look at:

☐ quantities of each type of waste generated, reasons why and its cost implications

☐ how wastes are being handled and stored

☐ recommendations for improving waste management.

Carrying out audits will provide valuable information to help set targets for improvement and will show how well waste management initiatives from the action plan are working on site.

Material recovery facilities (MRF) monitoring

It is good practice to ensure that exact recovery and recycling data from MRF's is obtained rather than average statistics, which will not accurately reflect the sites performance.

End of project assessment

Under the Site Waste Management Plans (England) Regulations 2008 at the completion of the project, the person responsible for the SWMP must undertake a full review of the plan and document expected performance, ie action plan, against the actual performance achieved. This review should include a comparison of the expected waste management costs versus actual waste costs. The plan must be kept for a minimum of two years following the completion of the project.

This review will provide valuable information internally that can be used on future projects to define SWMP action plans, and compare performance.

4.8.10   Waste disposal

Landfill tax

Any waste disposed of to landfill sites is subject to landfill tax. Landfill tax is regulated by HM Revenue and Customs and is designed to encourage businesses to produce less waste and to use alternative forms of waste management/disposal. It is a levy charged by weight and there are two rates: inactive and active waste. Inactive waste is charged at a substantially lower rate than active waste. If these waste types are mixed together the higher rate of tax will be charged on the whole load, so segregating waste saves money.

Waste arising from the following activities is exempt, subject to meeting certain conditions:

- some dredging activities
- quarrying and mining
- reclamation of contaminated land.

As at 2010 the cost of landfill tax for active wastes is £48 per tonne, and this will rise by £8 a year until at least 2013. Inactive wastes are charged at a lower cost for £2.50 per tonne. For further details on landfill tax refer to the Defra website <**www.defra.gov.uk**>

Non-hazardous waste

All non-hazardous waste leaving site must be accompanied by a waste transfer note, which needs to include the following information for controlled waste:

- description of the waste
- European Waste Catalogue (EWC) code
- how it is contained
- quantity of waste
- the place, date and time of transfer
- the name and address of both parties – site and either transfer or end disposal as applicable

☐ details of the permit, licence or exemption of the person receiving the
waste.

Copies of waste transfer notes need to be kept by the waste producer, the
waste carrier, waste broker (if applicable) and the waste disposer. These
records need to be kept for a minimum of two years for non-hazardous
wastes.

The transfer note records the transfer of waste between two parties. It does
not record the full journey of the waste and there is no requirement to
write the site of final disposal or recovery unless that is where the transfer
takes place.

Wastes requiring specialist services

Certain wastes require specialists to remove and dispose of them when they
are found on site, for example asbestos and sharps (see the following
sections). Removal of asbestos or sharps must be carried out under a
"specific method statement" that has been reviewed and approved by the
contractor.

Asbestos

Asbestos is a hazardous material that in the past was extensively used in
various applications including:

☐ insulation of pipes and boilers

☐ fire protection in panels, wall partitions, ceiling panels and around
structural steel work

☐ roof and wall cladding

☐ gutters, rainwater pipes and water tanks

☐ reinforced plastics and sealants

☐ bound in concrete.

During renovation or demolition the asbestos may be disturbed through
drilling, cutting or sanding. Such disturbance releases potentially harmful
fibres into the atmosphere that could cause serious health problems. If
asbestos is found or suspected, stop work immediately and contact a
specialist contractor to remove it. Specialist licences for transport and
disposal are required for asbestos wastes.

A contractor who buried 60 to 70 tonnes of asbestos in the ground during the demolition of disused pig units at the former Shepherd and Dog piggery in Nacton was ordered to pay £5500 in fines and Environment Agency costs by Ipswich Magistrates' Court. The roofs were corrugated bonded asbestos, which is classed as hazardous waste and should have been buried in a special sealed cell.

Sharps

A collective name for needles, syringes and other objects that can cause potential harm if the skin is pierced. If these are found on site do not touch any items and call a specialist contractor to remove them. Specialist licences for transport and disposal are required for sharps wastes.

4.8.11   Hazardous waste

If the producer, consignor or holder of hazardous waste wishes to have it removed then they need to complete a consignment note to move the waste (this includes premises that are exempt from registration). The hazardous waste consignment note travels with the waste to its final treatment or disposal option. Information that must be recorded on the consignment note includes:

☐   waste producer

☐   waste carrier

☐   premises code

☐   description of waste

☐   EWC code

☐   quantity (kg)

☐   chemical/biological components of waste and their concentrations

☐   physical form

☐   hazardous code(s)

☐   container type, number and size.

In England and Wales if more than 500 kg of hazardous waste per year on site is being produced, ie licensed/permitted, it must be ensured that the consignee (a person whom waste is transferred to for recovery or disposal) issues records to the site of waste disposed, including copies of consignment note and information of disposal, or recovery of waste. These returns must be retained by the holder at the registered site, or registered office after site closes.

The consignee must provide the Environment Agency with a quarterly return of all hazardous waste received by him/her. From a site perspective this will relate to transfer records and returns provided by the consignee.

Duty of care and SWMP

This is an example of where the Site Waste Management Plans (England) Regulations 2008 are applying good practice. The regulations require updates of all waste removed from site, including duty of care requirements. So a SWMP on site can help to assure that the duty of care requirements are being met.

Differences in Scotland, Wales and Northern Ireland

All movements of hazardous waste from sites in Northern Ireland must be accompanied by a uniquely coded consignment note obtained from the NIEA even if the waste is being transported directly to GB. Each note attracts a fee. In most cases this is £24. Three days before movement the NIEA must be notified with a copy of the consignment note partially completed in section A and B. A copy of the completed note must be sent to the NIEA once the waste has been received at a suitably authorised facility.

While similar processes take place in Scotland as described for England, at the time of publication enabling legislation is being produced by the Scottish Parliament. For example, legislation for site waste management plans is in place with a specific reference to waste prevention and management plans in Chapter 5 of the Climate Change (Scotland) Act 2009. For current details contractors are advised to consult SEPA. In Scotland, 72 hours notice is required to be given to SEPA before consigning any hazardous (special) waste.

Disposal of hazardous waste

Hazardous wastes can be accepted only at a particular hazardous landfill if they meet the relevant waste acceptance criteria (WAC) for that class of landfill and the waste acceptance procedures (WAP) are followed. Also, WAC testing may be used on general waste (eg to prove it is inert). There are three stages to assess this:

1   Ropean hazard criteria assessment.

2   Lids testing.

3   Aching testing.

All waste must be assessed. WAP consists of a three level hierarchy of assessment:

☐   Level 1 Basic characterisation: determination of short- and long-term leaching behaviour/characteristics of the waste.

☐   Level 2 Compliance testing: periodic testing to ensure waste is correctly predicted by Level 1 testing.

☐   Level 3 On-site verification: checks on site to confirm the waste is the same as that previously subjected to Level 2 testing and described in accompanying documents.

Basic characterisation is the responsibility of the producer who consigns the waste to landfill. Compliance testing and on-site verification are generally the responsibility of the landfill operator to ensure the waste complies with the WAC, environmental permit requirements of the landfill and the Landfill Directive (see Section 4.8.7).

Under the Hazardous Waste (England and Wales) Regulations 2005 (as amended in 2009), the Environment Agency must be notified of premises where more than 500 kg of hazardous waste will be produced in a year. Site can be registered with the Environment Agency via the internet, telephone or by paper. Once a site is registered it will be assigned a unique five digit code that needs to be put on all consignment notes. Registration of premises is only applicable in England and Wales and does not apply to premises producing hazardous waste in Northern Ireland or Scotland.

An important requirement of the regulations is to notify the Environment Agency of any premises (England and Wales only) producing hazardous waste (as notified above under transport and disposal). The regulations improve the management of hazardous waste from cradle to grave. Waste is defined under the regulations as either:

☐   non-hazardous

☐   hazardous (mirror entry) – waste that could be hazardous or non-hazardous, depending on its actual composition and concentration of "dangerous substances"

☐ hazardous (absolute) – waste that is hazardous, regardless of its composition or concentration of "dangerous substances".

The classification of waste and determination of disposal route under the Regulations involves the following steps:

1 Use EWC to classify the waste as either non-hazardous, hazardous (mirror entry) or hazardous (absolute).

2 Determine hazard level.

3 Determine WAC test and carry out either on site or at a treatment plant.

4 Demonstrate WAC test results meet legislative requirements.

5 Determine waste disposal route:

   ☐ inert waste landfill

   ☐ non-hazardous landfill

   ☐ non-reactive cell in non-hazardous landfill – asbestos and plasterboard

   ☐ hazardous waste landfill.

For further information on managing hazardous waste on site refer to <**www.hazardouswaste.org.uk**>.

Premises are exempt from the need to register if no more than 500 kg of hazardous waste is produced in a year. However, even where premises are exempt, collections of hazardous waste must still be made by a registered (or exempt) waste carrier, accompanied by a consignment note using a specific exemption code, and transferred to a facility that holds a suitable environmental permit (England and Wales only).

To move hazardous waste in Northern Ireland pre-notification is required and a consignment note must be obtained from the NIEA. Notification is required before movement can proceed. In Scotland, all hazardous (special) waste movements are required to be pre-notified to SEPA via a special waste consignment note.

In 2004 the EU Landfill Directive resulted in a significant decrease in the number of hazardous waste landfill sites in the UK. This resulted in higher transportation costs and higher gate charges being levied. Check the environmental regulators website to identify the nearest landfill sites that can accept hazardous waste.

4.8.12 Good practice checklists

Planning – SWMP

Identify a responsible person for developing, implementing and monitoring SWMP	
Identify and record waste stream (types, quantities)	
Identify and record waste disposal options and associated costs	

Planning – waste action plan

Review expected waste and disposal options with client, designers and/or architect. Agree actions to reduce expected wastes	
Update SWMP with action plan including cost estimates for waste expected	
Define facilities on site for requirements of SWMP and action plan	
Ensure sufficient space is allocated on site to meet waste management requirements	
Complete joint declaration of commitment to SWMP and action plan with client	
Obtain signage for skips (see <www.wasteawareconstruction.org>) and update signs to reflect the site, eg company name, contact details, waste transfer information	
Include SWMP and action plan requirements into induction material for communication	

Storing wastes properly on site

Segregate waste. Make this easy for site personnel to do, by providing several waste containers in a designated impermeable waste storage area and briefing personnel on their requirements	
Mark waste containers clearly with their intended contents	
Use containers suitable for their contents. Check that containers are not corroded or worn out	
Use covered skips to prevent spread of wind-blown wastes	

 Storage of hazardous waste

Check that the premises are registered as a producer of hazardous waste, if more than 500 kg is likely to be generated (England and Wales only)	
Ensure hazardous wastes are stored in suitable labelled containers away from sensitive receptors and away from the risk of damage by site traffic	
Hazardous waste must not be mixed with non-hazardous waste	
Do not mix different types of hazardous waste together	
Do not store wastes longer than is necessary to complete documentation to arrange their disposal	

 Handling and removing waste (on a confined site)

If removing waste from upper levels on buildings, transport using roller bins	
Store these bins in an area close to lifts	
Arrange for daily collection of bins	
Lower bins to ground floor only shortly before collection lorry arrives	

Duty of care

Check that a copy of the waste carrier's licence/environmental permit is available on site and that it is still valid. The waste carrier's licence/environmental permit should be accepted only if it has been endorsed by the appropriate environmental regulator	
The waste carrier must be licensed to carry waste	
The transfer notes should be completed in full and contain an accurate description of the waste, full European Waste Catalogue (EWC) code, and signed by the producer and carrier before waste leaves the site	
Keep copies of all transfer notes for waste sent off site for two years for inert and five years for hazardous	
Hazardous waste movements must be documented using consignment notes rather than the normal waste transfer note	
Carry out spot checks to ensure compliance with the duty of care including: ☐ following the waste carrier to ensure the waste does arrive at the agreed disposal site ☐ carrying out periodic audits on the waste carrier ☐ visiting the waste carrier's premises ☐ visiting agreed disposal site to confirm it is licensed/permitted to accept the waste.	

Monitoring and reporting waste

Update SWMP each time waste is removed from site (using transfer and consignment note records)	
Undertake monthly review of performance against action plan including targets and update records	
Report performance internally against action plan and seek improvements if required	
Complete performance assessment at end of project, including expected against actual waste generated, disposal, cost of disposal and any savings achieved	

4.8.13   Further guidance

CL:AIRE (2008) *The definition of waste: development of industry code of practice*, Contaminated Land: Applications in Real Environments (CL:AIRE), London

COVENTRY, S, SHORTER, B and KINGSLEY, M (2001) *Demonstrating waste minimisation benefits in construction* C536, CIRIA, London (ISBN: 978-0-86017-536-0)

COVENTRY, S, WOOLVERIDGE, C and HILLIER, S (1999) *The reclaimed and recycled materials handbook*, C513, CIRIA, London (ISBN: 978-0-86017-513-1)

CSS (1994) *Use of recycling for road pavement construction and maintenance*, ENG/1-94, County Surveyors' Society, Shrewsbury

ENVIRONMENT AGENCY (2005) *Guidance on sampling and testing of wastes to meet landfill waste acceptance procedures* (version 1), Environment Agency, Bristol *

ENVIRONMENT AGENCY (2005) *Waste – can you handle it? Requirements for the sampling and testing of waste destined for landfill. A guide for waste producers and waste managers.* GEHO040 5BIXJ-E-P, Environment Agency, Bristol *

ENVIRONMENT AGENCY (2006) *Guidance for waste destined for disposal in landfills* (version 2) Environment Agency, Bristol *

ENVIRONMENT AGENCY, SCOTTISH ENVIRONMENT PROTECTION AGENCY, ENVIRONMENT AND HERITAGE SERVICE (2008) *Technical Guidance WM2: Hazardous waste: interpretation of the definition and classification of hazardous waste*, second edition, version 2.2 Environment Agency, Bristol (ISBN: 1-84432-454-0) *

DEFRA (2008) *Non-statutory guidance for site waste management plans*, Department for Environment, Food and Rural Affairs, London *

HMSO (1996) *Waste management – the duty of care, code of practice*, Environmental Protection Act 1990 (Section 34) *

NETREGS (2008) *Site waste – it's criminal – a simple guide to site waste management plans* * Environment Agency, Northern Ireland Envrionment Agency and Scottish Environment Protection Agency, UK *

WRAP (2005) *The quality protocol for the production of aggregates from inert waste*, Waste and Resources Action Programme (WRAP), Banbury, Oxford *

*   denotes that a copy of the document is included on the accompanying resource CD

Relevant toolbox talks
(refer to Appendix A4)

Dust and air quality

Waste management

Storage of waste

Material handling and
housekeeping

Be a good neighbour

Segregation of waste

4.8.14   Legislation

The following table is a brief summary of applicable legislation to waste, including requirements and divided by UK region. Due to frequent legislative developments users should check <**www.netregs.gov.uk**> when using the table.

Legislation	Key requirements	Direct site requirements	Indirect requirements	Application time planning/during construction/post
England				
The Site Waste Management Plans (England) Regulations 2008	□ any project over £300 000 must have a SWMP □ prepare a plan that identifies all wastes created on site and defines plans to minimise waste production □ identify responsibilities for the delivery of the SWMP □ communicate SWMP to all appropriate parties and undertake necessary training □ monitor waste and update SWMP accordingly during construction □ review and close out SWMP at the end of construction process	□ create an SWMP and follow requirements	Ensure contractors and waste carriers comply with the SWMP	Planning During construction Post construction
Environmental Permitting Regulations (England & Wales) 2010 as amended	□ waste taken from site must be transported to a site with an appropriate environmental permit (incineration, landfill, waste to energy etc) □ storage of waste on site may require an environmental permit	□ ensure waste is disposed at a facility with an appropriate environmental permit for the waste carried from site □ ensure storage of any waste on site is in-line with permit requirements	N/A	Planning During construction

Legislation	Key requirements	Direct site requirements	Indirect requirements	Application time planning/during construction/post
Environmental protection (duty of care) Regulations 1991 as amended	□ any waste must stored properly, ie segregate and secure waste, and label accurately □ it is an offence for anyone to transport waste without being registered as a waste carrier with the Environment Agency □ waste transfer notes to be kept for a minimum of two years.	□ ensure waste carriers on site have an appropriate licence/permit for the waste carried from site □ ensure any waste to be stored is done so properly, ie segregate and secure waste, and label accurately. □ ensure waste transfer notes are kept for a minimum of two years □ ensure waste removed from site reaches the agreed destination	N/A	During construction Post construction
Hazardous Waste (England & Wales) Regulations 2005 as amended	□ no co-disposal or mixing of hazardous waste with other hazardous wastes or non-hazardous waste □ Environment Agency must be notified of all premises where hazardous wastes are produced above threshold of 500 kg per year □ hazardous waste consignment notes must be held for a minimum period of three years □ quarterly waste reporting by waste consignee	□ register as a hazardous waste producer if over 500 kg of hazardous waste per year □ do not mix hazardous waste with other hazardous wastes or non-hazardous waste □ hold hazardous waste consignment notes for a minimum of three year □ provide the Environment Agency with quarterly disposal and recovery information	N/A	Planning During construction Post construction

Legislation	Key requirements	Direct site requirements	Indirect requirements	Application time planning/during construction/post
Controlled Waste (Registration of Carriers and Seizure of Vehicles) (Amendment) Regulations 1998	☐ waste removed from site must be removed by a registered waste carrier	☐ when transferring waste from the site ensure that the appropriate waste carriers licence/permits are available	N/A	Planning During construction
Producer Responsibility Obligations (Packaging Waste) Regulations 2007 as amended	☐ the Regulations apply to all businesses involved in the packaging chain and who handle more than 50 tonnes of packaging material in a year and who have an annual turnover of £2m or more ☐ applies mainly to suppliers in the construction industry	☐ if a company places more than 50 tonnes of packaging into the packaging supply chain they should register with the Environment Agency or a compliance scheme and follow the guidance based on the amount of packaging involved	Likely to apply to large scale suppliers of construction materials	Planning During construction Post construction
List of Wastes (England) Regulations 2005	☐ provide six digit codes that must accompany waste as a means of classification	☐ hazardous waste consignments must be classified by their six digit waste code	N/A	During construction

Legislation	Key requirements	Direct site requirements	Indirect requirements	Application time planning/during construction/post
Wales				
Environmental Permitting Regulations (England & Wales) 2010 as amended	☐ waste taken from site must be transported to a site with an appropriate environmental permit (incineration, landfill, waste to energy etc)	☐ ensure waste is disposed at a facility with an appropriate environmental permit for the waste carried from site	N/A	Planning During construction
Environmental protection (duty of care) Regulations 1991 as amended	☐ any waste must be stored properly ie segregate and secure waste, and label accurately ☐ it is an offence for anyone to transport waste without being registered as a waste carrier with the Environment Agency ☐ ensure waste transfer notes are kept for a minimum of two years	☐ ensure waste carriers on site have an appropriate licence/permit for the waste carried from site ☐ ensure any waste to be stored properly, ie segregate and secure waste, and label accurately. ☐ ensure waste transfer notes are kept for a minimum of two years ☐ ensure waste removed from site reaches the agreed destination	N/A	During construction Post construction

Legislation	Key requirements	Direct site requirements	Indirect requirements	Application time planning/during construction/post
Hazardous Waste (England & Wales) Regulations 2005 as amended	☐ no co-disposal or mixing of hazardous waste with other hazardous wastes or non-hazardous waste ☐ Environment Agency must be notified of all premises where hazardous wastes are produced above threshold of 500 kg per year ☐ hazardous waste consignment notes must be held for a minimum period of three years ☐ quarterly waste reporting by waste consignee	☐ register as a hazardous waste producer if over 500 kg of hazardous waste per year ☐ do not mix hazardous waste with other hazardous wastes or non-hazardous waste ☐ hold hazardous waste consignment notes for a minimum of three years ☐ provide the Environment Agency with quarterly disposal and recovery information	N/A	Planning During construction Post construction
Controlled Waste (Registration of Carriers and Seizure of Vehicles) (Amendment) Regulations 1998	☐ waste removed from site must be removed by a licensed waste carrier	☐ when transferring waste from the site ensure that the appropriate waste carriers licence/environmental permits are available	N/A	Planning During construction

Legislation	Key requirements	Direct site requirements	Indirect requirements	Application time planning/during construction/post
Producer Responsibility Obligations (Packaging Waste) Regulations 2007 as amended	□ the Regulations apply to all businesses involved in the packaging chain and who handle more than 50 tonnes of packaging material in a year and who have an annual turnover of £2m or more □ applies mainly to suppliers in the construction industry	□ if the company places more than 50 tonnes of packaging into the packaging supply chain they should register with the Environment Agency or a compliance scheme and follow the guidance based on the amount of packaging involved	Likely to apply to large scale suppliers of construction materials	Planning During construction Post construction
List of Wastes (Wales) Regulations 2005	□ provide six digit codes that must accompany waste as a means of classification	□ hazardous waste consignments must be classified by their six digit waste code	N/A	During construction

Scotland

Legislation	Key requirements	Direct site requirements	Indirect requirements	Application time planning/during construction/post
Environmental protection (duty of care) Regulations 1991 as amended	☐ any waste to be stored properly ie segregate and secure waste, and label accurately ☐ it is an offence for anyone to transport waste without being registered as a waste carrier with SEPA ☐ ensure waste transfer notes are kept for a minimum of two years	☐ ensure waste carriers on site have an appropriate licence/permit for the waste carried from site ☐ ensure any waste to be stored properly ie segregate and secure waste, and label accurately ☐ ensure waste transfer notes are kept for a minimum of two years ☐ ensure waste removed from site reaches the agreed destination	N/A	During construction Post construction
Waste Management Licensing Regulations 1994 (as amended)	☐ prohibits the deposit, treatment or storage of controlled waste unless in accordance with a waste management licence. All those involved in the disposal, treatment or storage of controlled waste are required to be licensed by SEPA	☐ ensure waste is disposed at a facility with an appropriate waste management licence for the waste carried from site	N/A	Planning During construction

Legislation	Key requirements	Direct site requirements	Indirect requirements	Application time planning/during construction/post
The Pollution Prevention and Control (Scotland) Regulations 2000	☐ regulates pollution prevention control (PPC) facilities in Scotland	☐ ensure waste is disposed at a facility with an appropriate PPC permit	N/A	During construction
The Special Waste (Scotland) Regulations 1996 (as amended)	☐ defines special wastes and sets out the requirements for disposal of special waste	☐ do not mix special waste with other special wastes or non-hazardous waste ☐ hold special waste consignment notes for a minimum of three years ☐ provide SEPA with quarterly disposal and recovery information	N/A	Planning During construction Post construction
Producer Responsibility Obligations (Packaging Waste) Regulations 2007 as amended	☐ the regulations apply to all businesses involved in the packaging chain and who handle more than 50 tonnes of packaging material in a year and who have an annual turnover of £2m or more ☐ applies mainly to suppliers in the construction industry	☐ if the company places more than 50 tonnes of packaging into the packaging supply chain they should register with SEPA or a compliance scheme and follow the guidance based on the amount of packaging involved	Likely to apply to large scale suppliers of construction materials	Planning During construction Post construction

Legislation	Key requirements	Direct site requirements	Indirect requirements	Application time planning/during construction/post
The Landfill (Scotland) Regulations 2003	☐ regulates Scottish landfill sites	☐ ensure waste removed from site to landfill is disposed in a registered landfill	N/A	During construction
Northern Ireland				
Waste Management Licensing Regulations (Northern Ireland) 2003	☐ prohibits the deposit, treatment or storage of controlled waste unless in accordance with a waste management licence. All those involved in the disposal, treatment or storage of controlled waste are required to be licensed	☐ ensure waste is disposed at a facility with an appropriate waste management licence for the waste carried from site	N/A	Planning During construction
The Pollution Prevention and Control (Northern Ireland) Regulations 2003	☐ regulates pollution prevention control (PPC) facilities in NI	☐ ensure waste is disposed at a facility with an appropriate PPC permit	N/A	During construction

Legislation	Key requirements	Direct site requirements	Indirect requirements	Application time planning/during construction/post
Hazardous Waste (Northern Ireland) Regulations 2005 as amended	☐ no co-disposal or mixing of hazardous waste with other hazardous wastes or non-hazardous waste ☐ NIEA must be notified of all premises where hazardous wastes are produced above threshold of 500 kg per year ☐ hazardous waste consignment notes must be held for a minimum period of three years ☐ quarterly waste reporting by waste consignee	☐ register as a hazardous waste producer if over 500 kg of hazardous waste per year ☐ do not mix hazardous waste with other hazardous wastes or non-hazardous waste ☐ hold hazardous waste consignment notes for a minimum of three years ☐ provide the NIEA with quarterly disposal and recovery information	N/A	Planning During construction Post construction
Producer Responsibility Obligations (Packaging Waste) Regulations (Northern Ireland) 2007 as amended	☐ the Regulations apply to all businesses involved in the packaging chain and who handle more than 50 tonnes of packaging material in a year and who have an annual turnover of £2m or more ☐ applies mainly to suppliers in the construction industry	☐ if the company places more than 50 tonnes of packaging into the packaging supply chain they should register with the NIEA or a compliance scheme and follow the guidance based on the amount of packaging involved	Likely to apply to large scale suppliers of construction materials	Planning During construction Post construction
The Landfill (Northern Ireland) Regulations 2003	☐ regulates NI landfill sites	☐ ensure waste removed from site to landfill is disposed in a registered landfill	N/A	During construction

Legislation	Key requirements	Direct site requirements	Indirect requirements	Application time planning/during construction/post
List of Wastes Regulations (Northern Ireland) 2005	☐ provide six digit codes that must accompany waste as a means of classification	☐ hazardous waste consignments must be classified by their six digit waste code	N/A	During construction

4.9   Water

4.9.1.   Why is water management important?

Waters, including rivers, streams, ditches, ponds, lakes/lochs/loughs, groundwater and coastal waters up to three miles offshore have legal protection from harm and pollution. Pollution can result from any of the following entering a body of surface or groundwater: any poisonous, noxious or polluting matter or any waste matter (including silt, cement, concrete, oil, petroleum spirit, chemicals, solvents, sewage and other polluting matter) or other harmful activities detrimentally affecting the status of a water body. Under the EU Water Framework Directive, the status of a water body can be affected not only by chemical pollution, but also by activities directly or indirectly affecting ecology including changes in physico-chemical parameters such as temperature, turbidity and dissolved oxygen or physical modifications to the hydrology or morphology of a water body. For example, activities such as engineering works on inland waters may harm the integrity of the waters or their environs such as river-banks.

It is vital to manage sites properly to protect the water environment and water supplies. If waters are polluted or otherwise harmed, or if unacceptable wastes are disposed of to sewer systems, the management, company, subcontractors and clients could end up in court. Also, they may be liable for damages to industries or other third parties using water downstream.

A Holsworthy man was ordered to pay £3000 in fines and costs after diesel oil escaped from his agricultural contractor's yard into a nearby stream. Fuel had been leaking from the stop valve of a fuel tank and overflowing from a storage drum.

4.9.2   Water pollution

Water regulation applies the polluter pays principle. For example, the polluter can be responsible for paying any fine through strict liability, court costs, and also for the cost of clean-up, which is often greater than the fine. Directors can be held personally responsible and can be fined up to £40 000 and imprisoned for up to three months or two years on indictment and/or an unlimited fine.

A site does not need to be next to a river or other water body to cause a problem. Any pollutants getting into subsoil surface water drain or groundwater can end up in a river even if it is miles away. Often these pollutants can be tracked back to their source.

Even a small amount of material can be a pollutant and one of the most common sources of contamination from construction sites is silt solids. For example, the normal limits set by the environmental regulator for suspended solids are typically 30–40 mg/I (50 mg/l in Northern Ireland). This is about the equivalent of mixing half a tablespoon of soil in a bath full of water. Another common pollutant from sites is oil. Again, pollution does not necessarily involve large quantities. For example, five litres of oil can cover an area of water equivalent to four football pitches.

During the upgrading of the M74(M) in south-west Scotland, discharges from the construction site into top quality salmonid rivers contained suspended solids concentrations as high as 46 800 mg/l. These high concentrations of suspended solids, derived from silt, resulted in the contractors being fined £40 000 for the offences.

High levels of silt can clog the gills of fish and ultimately lead to their death. Also, it can smother invertebrates and sensitive plant life, which are themselves a food source for fish. When deposited on the stream bed, silt may prevent fish from spawning successfully and suffocate eggs. Silt levels as low as 15 mg/I can harm juvenile fish. Various measures can be taken to prevent silt from entering water including the installation of a silt fence as illustrated in Figure 4.28.

Figure 4.28
Silt fence (courtesy
Galliford Try)

A contractor was found liable for causing oil pollution of the Grand
Union Canal after a tap was removed from an oil storage tank. Despite
the contractor blaming vandals the Magistrates agreed with the
Environment Agency that the site had poor security and the company
was fined £7000 and had to pay costs of more than £11 000.

Pollutants can damage the water environment in other ways, as shown in
Table 4.4.

Table 4.4
Common water pollutants and their effects on the aquatic environment

Common pollutants of water	Adverse affect on aquatic environment
Silt	Reduces water quality, clogs fish gills, covers aquatic plants. Silt also injures fish by its abrasive action. It can stunt aquatic plant growth, limiting oxygen supplies, shelter and a food source
Bentonite (very fine silt)	Reduces water quality, clogs fish gills, covers aquatic plants
Cement or concrete wash water (highly alkaline)	Changes the chemical balance, toxic to fish and other wildlife
Detergents	Removes dissolved oxygen, can be toxic to fish and other wildlife
Hydrocarbons, eg oil, diesel	Suffocates aquatic life, damaging to water supplies including industrial abstractions

Contaminants that disperse quickly are difficult to control and treat. They are easily transported in waters and the effects are likely to be significant. Some contaminants can smother the surface of watercourses (or standing waters such as lakes or lochs) depleting oxygen and leading to fish deaths or harm to other wildlife or third party interests. Notify and seek advice immediately from the environmental regulator if spillages occur.

A company and its principal director were together fined in excess of £3800 after having pleaded guilty to polluting the Battleton Brook at Hinton on Green. Enforcement officers found that the immediate cause of the incident was the digging of a trench by the director that diverted the slurry off the track and into a nearby watercourse.

4.9.3   Water pollution prevention

All sites have the potential to pollute watercourses so a standard approach should be adopted at the earliest stage of the project. Survey the site through a combination of desktop reviews of plans, site drawings, contract documents and reviews of local authority information, and by walking around the site for a physical check.

Use the source–pathway–receptor model to identify the site risk as shown in Table 4.5 (see Section 4.4.2 for further details).

Table 4.5

Example source-pathway-receptor model

Source	Pathway	Receptor
Earthworks –silt pollution from vehicle movements	Wash off across roads	Surface water drain

After undertaking this process the scale and significance of the problem can be assessed and the most suitable control measures for the site can be defined. If following Table 4.5 new columns should be added for recording controls and monitoring requirements.

Controls should be applied in a hierarchical manner for each pollution item identified, ie try applying control measures at source, if not possible at pathway, if not possible receptor.

When assessing the site for pollution potential, pay particular attention to sources of diffuse pollution. Diffuse pollution is the release of (potential) pollutants from a range of activities that individually may have no effect on the water environment, but at the scale of a catchment can have a significant impact (ie on water quality and wildlife). So, while an individual instance of silt pollution from a site may not have a significant effect, many instances across the site into the same water catchment will be significant.

Carillion JM Limited and Wilson Bowden Developments Limited were ordered to pay £21 000 for poor planning and inadequate pollution prevention measures resulting in water offences being committed at a construction development site at Castlewood Grange (near South Normanton). Runoff containing debris from the construction process unlawfully entered a nearby Brook causing a downstream increase in the concentration of suspended solids. The enforcement officers found that the non-existence of a settlement lagoon to treat runoff from the site or a balancing pond were the immediate causes of the polluting incidents.

Pollution prevention control measures

Drainage

Identify all drainage on site and use colour coding to distinguish them: blue for surface water, red for foul water and a red "C" for combined drainage systems. This ensures that all those working on the site are aware of the type of drain in the event of a pollution incident. Depending on the types of drains, where they are on site and potential sources of pollution control measures can be applied such as placing interceptors in drains to catch oils or placing bunding or silt traps around drains to prevent silt runoff.

Avoiding spillages

There are many precautions that can be taken to avoid spillages. These are outlined in Chapter 3 and include:

☐ use of secondary containment, eg bunds around oil storage tanks, which may be a legal requirement

☐ use of drip trays around mobile plant

☐ supervising all deliveries and refuelling activities

☐ designating and using specific impermeable refuelling areas isolated from surface water drains.

Forward or risk planning can ensure a speedy emergency response if things do go wrong. For example, sandbags can be used as a barrier to protect sensitive areas, or to block off drains during refuelling. Also, they are effective for controlling and mopping up some types of spillages. Any absorbent material that becomes contaminated will have to be disposed of as hazardous waste (see Section 4.8.11).

Managing effluent from vehicles and boot washing

Usually it is preferable to wash vehicles and plant at specialist facilities rather than on site. Where this is not possible the following options are shown in order of best environmental option:

☐ carry out cleaning in a bunded area and recycle the water, but not if contaminants are being washed off

☐ discharge waste water to the foul sewer (with the consent of the sewerage provider)

   ☐   collect water in a sealed tank for removal from site by a licensed waste disposal contractor.

Vehicle wheels may need to be washed on site to avoid mud on public roads. A specific wheel washing facility (Figure 4.29) should be used that should store the water, with either a discharge to the foul sewer or, if contaminated, collection by tanker. Where a site is not contaminated, water recycling wheel washing systems are available where only the collected silt needs to be removed.

Figure 4.29
On-site wheel wash facility (courtesy Bovis Lend Lease)

Facilities should be provided for site workers to wash their boots (Figure 4.30) to remove mud. This is vital on contaminated sites. Again this should follow the procedures in place for vehicle wheel washing.

Figure 4.30
On-site bootwash
facility (courtesy
Morrison Construction)

Do not allow water containing detergents to enter either surface water drains or other surface or groundwater bodies.

In exceptional circumstances, discharge to a surface water body may be permitted with the consent of the environmental regulator. However, this would typically require pre-treatment (for example, silt settlement and oil separation) and it may be difficult to control quality.

If tools and equipment need to be washed, ensure that this is undertaken well away from any waters or surface water drains on an area of hardstanding to avoid infiltration of potential pollutants into soils.

Preventing and managing runoff and silty water

Surface water runoff may cause water management or pollution problems. For example, more than 25 tonnes of sediment can be eroded per hectare off site in a year. On many sites, a high priority is therefore to remove the potential for runoff, for instance by considering the following:

1   Can the proposal be altered to minimise land clearing and land shaping?

2   Can the proposal be altered to allow permanent stabilisation of disturbed areas as soon as land shaping is complete?

3   Can undisturbed areas be used as sediment buffer zones either during construction or on a long-term basis as appropriate?

4   Can site entry points be located so as to minimise soil contamination of vehicles, and is it possible to allow the early establishment of all-weather parking areas?

5   Is it possible to locate imported material and soil stockpiles in areas that minimise on-site traffic movement?

6   Can the works be sequenced to make best use of existing buffer zones and stabilised areas?

7   Can the development be staged so that most of the ground disturbance occurs outside periods of high saturation?

If runoff is still likely to occur, surface water will need to be managed so that it does not run into excavations, over disturbed ground or onto haul roads. Steps should be taken to ensure that the water collection system is adequate to allow for the controlled release of storm flows. Ensure to keep hard standing areas and surface roads clean from mud and oil build-up, and keep stockpiles covered.

Periods of heavy rain can dramatically increase surface water runoff giving very high pollutant loads. Some areas of the UK are subject to considerably higher rainfall than others, eg west coasts. This factor should be taken into account when considering the management of runoff. Another important factor is soil types on site. Clay soils are much more difficult to remove from site runoff once mobilised than sandy soils. So, construction activities in high rainfall areas with clay soils have the potential to cause more serious environmental harm to waters than contracts in low rainfall areas with sandy soils. Issues relating to the potential of pollution from runoff should be fully considered on every site.

Silt curtains (see Figure 4.31) work by preventing runoff flowing over ground. However, it is important not to rely on silt fences to remove sediment from concentrated flows such as pipe discharges or in flow watercourses. Adequate scour protection (eg rock mattresses, geofabrics) should be provided at points of concentrated discharge to spread flows and reduce velocities minimising damage and mobilisation of sediment.

Figure 4.31
Silt curtain (courtesy Galliford Try)

Fences cause a physical barrier, capturing the water and enabling it to seep into the ground where it is naturally filtered as it flows down hill. If correctly installed, silt fences can prevent erosion and stop silt laden runoff entering watercourses. Correct installation of silt fences is vital. The silt fence should be shaped and installed so that it will catch runoff, without the water flowing underneath or around the edge. Also, the shape of the silt fence will depend on the gradient of the slope. It is important that the bottom of the geotextile is dug into the ground so that water does not simply flow under the barrier.

Grips, sumps, straw bales and sediment traps can be installed to capture silt. Each of these should be regularly maintained to ensure that they remain effective (ie do not become blocked) and not increase the likelihood of an incident occurring.

How and what to monitor

Undertaking the chemical analysis of water samples for trace quantities of contaminants or for particular pollutants is a specialised task. However, the visual appearance of a water sample can indicate potential problems associated with a water sample, for example:

☐   unusual levels of turbidity or colour

☐   odour

☐   presence of oil film.

The use of pH papers and test strips can be used to indicate the presence of specific contaminants on site. For instance, high pH rinse waters from cement batching plants or grouting works can be toxic to aquatic life and may cause a severe pollution incident. This can be identified easily through the use of pH papers that show a colour change in response to differing acidity or alkalinity.

Regular visual checks should be undertaken to check for changes in water colour, changes in water transparency; oil sheen to the surface of the water, scum or foam build-up on the surface, and signs of dead plants or animals. Monitoring will have to be carried out if conditions are specified in trade effluent and discharge consents. This may include flow rate, suspended solids, chemical or biological oxygen demand, or chemical constituents.

4.9.4   Emergency preparedness and response

All site personnel should be aware of the appropriate action in the event of an emergency, such as the spillage of potentially polluting substances. A spill response plan/procedure should be developed for the site (see Section 2.4). For details on appropriate fuel storage preparedness measures see Section 4.5.5. Any environmental damage to surface water or groundwater must be reported to the environmental regulator unless it can be remedied immediately and steps must be taken to limit the damage caused any such by incidents.

4.9.5   Dealing with water pollution – considering the options

To establish the best approach for the site, review the following prioritised options. Those at the top of the list are likely to be least expensive and should minimise the risk of accidental pollution. However, when considering these options, account should be taken of the size of the construction site, annual rainfall data, soil types, site topography and flow paths during the various stages of construction, and the sensitivity of the waters in or around the site (eg do they have environmental designations, and are they used by third parties?):

1   Pump to grassland or other soakaway – well away from excavations to avoid recirculation through the ground. The silty water should contain no chemical pollutants (cheapest).

2   Pump to sewer – consent from the sewage provider is required. This is unlikely to be allowed in Northern Ireland.

3   Pump to settlement tank/constructed ponds or wetlands maximising retention time.

4   Pass through a filtration system.

5   Use flocculants in conjunction with settlement tank/ponds.

6   Pump into a tanker and dispose of off site (most expensive).

The preferred options will depend on several factors, including:

☐   the quantities of water involved

☐   whether areas are available for storage and treatment

☐   the level of any charges to be levied by the sewerage provider

☐   the degree of contamination of the water

☐   sensitivity, quality and flow of the receiving watercourse

☐   the characteristics of the sediment.

Remember, silt arising from clay soils is vastly more difficult to remove than sandy particles before discharge to controlled waters. Also, consider the amount of rainfall that is likely in a particular area.

Obtain the approval of the environmental regulator and the landowner before doing anything.

Pumping to grasslands/fields

This option is only suitable for water that is unpolluted aside from its silt content. It may be necessary to allow water temperatures to rise by storing in a lagoon before discharge onto crops. Typical infiltration rates are given in Table 4.6 for various soils.

Table 4.6
Typical infiltration rates for different soil types
(reproduced from Bettess, 1996)

Soil type	Infiltration co-efficient (m/h)
Gravel	10–1000
Sand	0.1–100
Loamy sand	0.01–1
Sandy loam	0.05–0.5
Loam	0.001–0.1
Silt loam	0.0005–0.05
Chalk	0.001–100
Cut-off point for most infiltration drainage systems	0.001
Sandy clay loam	0.001–0.01
Silty clay loam	0.00005–0.0005
Clay	<0.0001
Till	0.00001–0.01
Rock	0.00001–0.1

To get an accurate infiltration rate carry out appropriate measurements, eg using the BRE soakaway test (see BRE 1999).

Settlement tanks/lagoons/ponds/wetlands

A settlement lagoon (pond or tank) (as shown in Figure 4.32) works by retaining water in an undisturbed state long enough for suspended solids to settle out. The clean water then either flows out at the discharge point or is pumped out. Usually it is necessary to retain the water in the settlement tank for two to three hours at maximum flow rate (see Table 4.7). However, finer particulate matter (eg fine sand) may require a longer retention time and possibly larger lagoons. An idea of the required retention time can be obtained by leaving a sample of the contaminated water to stand in a clear glass bottle. Compare this sample to a prepared sample of a concentration equal to the consented discharge. As a general rule, when the contaminated water sample looks as clear as the sample representing the consented discharge, it may be discharged. Settlement tanks should only be used with low flow, they are not effective with large volumes.

Figure 4.32
Settlement lagoon
(courtesy Galliford Try)

Where sufficient ground is available it may be possible to create a wetland around the pond to allow further treatment of the runoff. Where sustainable drainage systems (SuDS) are to be utilised for surface water management from the final development it may be possible to construct such features at the start of the construction project with the aim of their being retained as a permanent feature.

Table 4.7
Typical dimensions of a settlement tank/lagoon for a three-hour settling time

Pump diameter	Discharge rate	Length	Width
6 in pump	3000 l/min	60 m	20 m
	6000 l/min	80 m	27 m
4 in pump	1000 l/min	30 m	10 m
2500 l/min	2500 l/min	50 m	17 m

Note:
Assuming 1 m-deep ponds, where the length = three times the width

March

> Consider installing a spare settlement tank/lagoon on site, so that it can be used an as emergency overflow or when the main tank is being cleaned.

Filtration

Discharges with fairly coarse particles (but no other pollutants) and relatively small flows may be treated easily and cheaply by passing them through steel tanks or even skips (see Figure 4.33) filled with a suitable filter, such as fine single size aggregates (five to 10 mm), geotextiles or straw bales. Filtration socks can be added for further treatment. If this solution is used there should be careful control of the discharge quality and a mechanism to close down the flow. Discharge should then be to land (with landowners permission), to sewer (with water company permission), or to surface waters (with the environmental regulator's permission).

Figure 4.33
Water siltbusters in use
(courtesy Bouygues
Travaux Publics)

Flocculation

If no alternative treatment is available (whether due to the material characteristics, lack of space or lack of suitable discharge locations), the use of settlement tanks together with flocculants (and/or coagulants) can be an effective solution, particularly to aid the settlement of fine silts. This approach needs specialist advice on the design of the system, the size and dosing rates etc, and careful supervision to avoid failures of the system. Flocculants commonly used include aluminium sulphate and ferric sulphate. If applied incorrectly they can cause pollution.

4.9.6   Water abstraction and discharge

If there is a need to abstract water or to discharge to either surface water (eg river, stream, estuary) or groundwater, the regulator should be contacted to confirm whether a permit or consent will be required (the terminology is different in different regions).

Abstracting water

Some construction activities, for example concrete batching or dust suppression, require water to be abstracted from surface water or groundwater.

Abstraction needs to be licensed/permitted because water is a resource and over abstraction, or impeding flows can lead to:

☐   shortages in water supply

☐   increased pollution due to reduced dilution of pollutants

☐   damage to habitats.

Each application is considered for its potential impacts based on national and regional considerations.

Contact the environmental regulator for information. In Scotland any abstraction of more than 10 m³ per day will need to be registered or licensed with SEPA under the Water Environment (Controlled Activities) (Scotland) Regulations 2005.

> A consortium of developers comprising Allison Homes Eastern Ltd, Persimmon Homes (East Midlands) Ltd and Stamford Homes Ltd was fined in excess of £26 000 for failing to comply with the terms of their discharge consent and allowing polluted water carrying 10 times the allowable level of ammonia and four times the permissible solids concentration to enter a stream close to their housing development. The investigating officers found that a lack of maintenance of the sewage treatment works (and particularly desludging) was a major contributor to the incident and the resulting penalties.

Discharging water

Discharges should only be made to drains following formal legal approval by way of a licence or consent/permit from the environmental regulator:

☐   foul water sewer – effluent discharge consent required from sewerage provider

☐   waters (from surface water drains or any other temporary/permanent outfalls installed to serve the site) – discharge consent from environmental regulator.

If the discharge of water is necessary this should be to the foul sewer rather than to a surface water drain.

Discharge consents/permits/licences can be obtained from the environmental regulator, but can take up to four months to obtain, or even longer if there are representations made by third parties/the public. It is important to plan ahead to avoid delays. Even with a consent/licence, allowable pollution limits will be low.

Water used on site may be contaminated with pollutants that cannot be discharged to the sewer. So, it will have to be pumped into a tanker and taken off site for disposal to an appropriately licensed disposal facility, adding extra costs to the project. Figure 4.34 outlines the steps to follow when disposing of water on site.

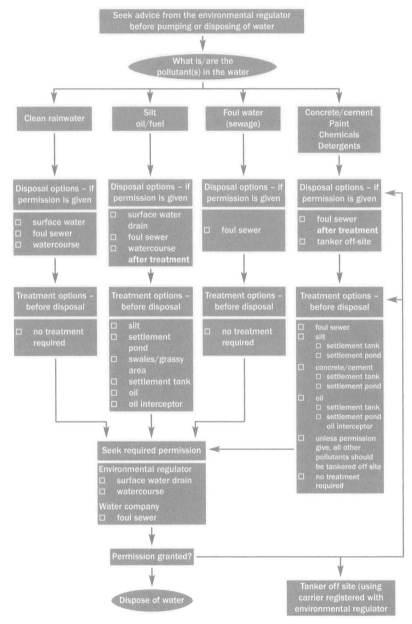

Figure 4.34
Treatment of site water procedure

Gladman Developments Limited was fined and ordered to pay in excess of £10 000 for polluting a County Durham stream by discharging extremely polluted water from their site on the Drum Industrial Estate without a discharge consent. The company failed to heed instructions from Northumbrian Water Limited to stop discharging despite being ordered to do so.

4.9.7   Using water wisely

Water efficiency is an increasingly significant issue with limits being placed on the quantity of supplies of fresh water for use by people, but also reduced water quality and quantity for habitats and species.

It is good practice on site to consider water use needs and to seek to reduce these wherever possible, to reduce the need to use potable water from taps, or to seek abstraction permits/licenses. There are many ways that water efficiency can be achieved, for instance changing construction process to reduce the need to damp down.

4.9.8   Sustainable drainage systems (SuDS)

Traditional drainage systems can lead to an increased risk of flooding through surface water runoff, to contamination of water bodies with pollutants, or to the diversion of water away from natural groundwater systems. Often, the inclusion of SuDS in a development is a stated policy aim of the regulators for final developments, but also SuDS can be considered for use during the construction phases of projects.

If SuDS are to be used as part of the final development for surface water disposal or management, it may be possible to install ponds and wetlands as the initial phase of construction allowing site drainage to be managed accordingly. Perhaps following a clean out, the ponds and wetlands can remain on site to serve the development once built.

In south-west Scotland and in Cumbria, ponds were used for the treatment of runoff from the construction of the M74 and the M6. Once construction was completed, the ponds were slightly modified and in some cases wetlands were included but otherwise, the facilities installed for treating runoff from the construction site were retained as a permanent SuDS feature for treating highway drainage.

4.9.9   Working over or near to water

Consent/licence may be required from the environmental regulator for any works over or near to water. Particular care should be taken to avoid the increased risk of water pollution. In addition to the measures described in Section 4.9.3, good practice includes:

☐   ensuring the comprehensive risk assessments undertaken included water-related risks, and that the risk management plans are implemented

☐   use of decking/barges below the works (acting as a bund in case of spillage)

☐   availability and, if necessary, use of primary and secondary booms to contain pollutants in the event of substances entering the water

☐   erecting dust screens on bridges.

Figure 4.35
Pollution prevention
(courtesy Kier)

Temporary works

In England and Wales, the Environment Agency needs at least seven days notice of any intention to temporarily or permanently divert the flow of a watercourse, to carry out works over or within the river channel or to begin operations in the river channel.

Obtain approval from the Environment Agency for all temporary works that involve construction, erection, re-erection or modification during work that:

☐ may interfere with the bed or banks or flood channel of any watercourse

☐ is within 8 m of the bank of any main river

☐ is within 16 m of any tidal defence.

In Scotland, SEPA needs to be notified in advance of similar works and depending on the scale of the activity a licence may be required. If the works do require a licence this can take up to four months to issue and even longer if representations are made by third parties.

In Northern Ireland NIEA and Rivers Agency would need to be contacted for consultation before any river works are started.

4.9.10   Good practice checklists

Know the site

Identify potential pollution pathways and receptors on site

Define suitable controls to prevent pollution entering pathways and reaching receptors

Check the annual rainfall data, soil types, site topography and flow paths during the various planned stages of construction

Identify site drainage as surface, combined or foul water and suitably colour code and mark on the site plan

Protect/cover all drains

Ensure that the correct connections are being made with either foul sewers, surface water drains or combined systems

Identify all water bodies, gain appropriate consents and put measures in place to fulfil the requirements of the consent

Abstracting water

Ensure the site has a licence/permit to abstract water from groundwater, a stream or river etc

Ensure the site complies with the abstraction licence/permit

Discharging water

Check that appropriate consents/permits/licence for disposal of all water are in place, and that personnel are aware of the quantity and quality of water that can be discharged

Check for any visible sign or smell of pollution in waters at or near the site

Water needs to be treated effectively before disposal

If a settlement tank (or lagoon) is being used, check it is working properly

How and what to monitor

Establish a regular monitoring procedure for water discharged from the site and keep records (turbidity/flow rate)	
Undertake daily visual inspection of watercourses on and near to a site for signs of pollution	
Check outfalls and pipework daily to ensure they are clean and clear of litter etc	

Avoiding spillages

Store liquids, solids and powders appropriately away from drains and waters, and in secondary containment	
Store solvents, chemicals or paints in accordance with their COSHH datasheets	
Appropriate spill kits should be available (eg oil only, chemical or general use) and adequately stocked	

Emergency preparedness and response

Ensure site personnel know who to contact in the event of a spillage, what to do and from where to get equipment	
Adopt and test an emergency response plan/procedure	
Report environmental damage that cannot be rectified immediately to the environmental regulator and takes steps to remedy the damage caused	
Nominate a spill contractor to deal with major incidents	

Managing effluent

Wash out concrete lorries in a suitably contained designated area	
Ensure designated washout area is at least 10 m away from drains and waters	
Protect surface and groundwaters from washout	
Put a plan/procedure in place to dispose of washout cost-effectively	

Managing runoff and silty water

When undertaking earthworks ensure there is a filter (or buffer) strip left to protect surface water	
Regularly check waters for signs of harm (if applicable)	
Look for any visible signs of discolouration in waters (if applicable) at or near the site	
Silty or discoloured water should not be discharged from the site	
Surface water runoff should not be directly entering waters or drains	
Monitor any water treatment methods to ensure their effectiveness	
If a settlement tank is used, ensure that water is not moving too fast and/or overflowing (other than at the discharge point)	
If necessary, erect silt fences along the downslope or sideslope of disturbed areas	
If straw bales are used, ensure they are securely fixed	

Working over or near to water

Avoid storing fuel in vessels near water	
Ensure that no site works are occurring within 10 m of the edge of waters	
Check that the banks or bed of waters outside the area of the works are not being affected by discharges or vehicle movements etc	
Spray, dust or other airborne materials should be prevented from entering waters	
Approaches to the watercourse should be kept free from the build up of mud	
If using a cofferdam to retain water, it needs to be in good condition and working effectively	
Regularly check waters downstream of the works to see if these are silted or discoloured or if there is an oily sheen visible on the water	
Ensure spill kits are adequately stocked	
Personnel should be aware of the location of spill kits and know how to use these properly	
Mitigation measures should be put in place in the event of an emergency (eg booms across river). Ensure the environmental regulator is contacted immediately	

Settlement tank/lagoon

Design

The size of the tank/lagoon should be adequate for the settlement time required and the rate at which water flows or is pumped into it	
Install a long, narrow, shallow settlement lagoon to ensure maximum retention time of all water in the lagoon	

Operation

Obtain a consent/licence to pump clean water from the surface of settlement lagoons into waters or a designated discharge point	
Clean the entry chamber periodically to prevent a build-up of silt	
Regularly inspect/monitor the outflow quality	

Dealing with water in excavations

Measures should be put in place to prevent water from entering excavations	
Inform the environmental regulator before undertaking any excavation below the water table, including any site dewatering	
Control water in excavations by stone-filled edge drains leading to sumps	
To manage groundwater flowing into excavations, install cut off ditches, walls or well point dewatering	
Obtain a discharge consent/licence for the disposal of water from excavations	

Pontoons and barges

All fuel tanks to be secure and safe on the vessel so that there is no chance of collision damage or accidental spillage overboard	
Contaminated bilge water should be pumped to suitable facilities ashore or absorbents used	

4.9.11 Further guidance

Regulatory guidance

Pollution prevention guidance notes: 1 to 8, 18, 21, 23, 36, 27 (see Appendix A3)

SEPA, ENVIRONMENT AGENCY, NORTHERN IRELAND ENVIRONMENT AGENCY, CIRIA (2000) *Masonry bunds for oil storage tanks*, Environment Agencies Joint Guidelines *

SEPA, ENVIRONMENT AGENCY, NORTHERN IRELAND ENVIRONMENT AGENCY, CIRIA (2000) *Concrete bunds for oil storage tanks*, Environment Agencies Joint Guidelines *

Other guidance

BETTESS, R (1996) *Infiltration drainage – manual of good practice*, R156, CIRIA, London (ISBN: 978-0-86017-457-8)

BRE (1999) *Soakaway design*, Digest 365, BRE Publications, Garston (ISBN: 1-86081-604-5)

BRITISH WATERWAYS (2009) *Code of practice for works affecting British waterways*, British Waterways, UK *

BUDD, M, JOHN, S, SIMM, J and WILKINSON, M (2003) *Coastal and marine environmental site guide*, C584, CIRIA, London (ISBN: 978-0-86017-584-1)

DEFRA (2004) *Groundwater Protection Code: solvent use and storage*, PB 9849, Department for the Environment, Food and Rural Affairs, London *

ENVIRONMENT AGENCY (2000) *Decommissioning redundant boreholes and wells*, National Groundwater and Contaminated Land Centre, Environment Agency, Solihull*

MASON, P A, AMIES, H J, SANGARAPILLAI, G et al (1997) *Construction of bunds for oil storage tanks*, R163, CIRIA, London (ISBN: 978-0-86017-468-4)

MASTERS-WILLIAMS, H et al (2001) *Control of water pollution from construction sites. Guidance for consultants and contractors*, C532, CIRIA, London (ISBN: 978-0-86017-532-2)

MURNANE, E et al (2002) *Control of water pollution from construction sites – guide to good practice*, SP156, CIRIA, London (ISBN: 978-0-86017-807-1)

MURNANE, E, HEAP, A and SWAIN, A (2006) *Control of water pollution from linear construction projects. Technical guidance*, C648, CIRIA, London (ISBN: 978-0-86017-648-0)

MURNANE, E, HEAP, A and SWAIN, A (2006) *Control of water pollution from linear construction projects. Site guide,* C649, CIRIA, London (ISBN: 978-0-86017-649-7)

SEPA (2008) *The Water Environment (Controlled Activities) (Scotland) Regulations 2005, a practical guide,* Scottish Environment Protection Agency, Stirling *

*   denotes that a copy of the document is included on the accompanying resource CD

> **Relevant toolbox talks**
> **(refer to Appendix A4)**
>
> **Spill control**
>
> **Water pollution prevention (fuel and oil)**
>
> **Water pollution: silt**
>
> **Water pollution: cement and concrete**
>
> **Oil/diesel storage**
>
> **Bentonite**
>
> **Pumping and overpumping**
>
> **Washing down plant and machinery**

4.9.12   Legislation

The following table is a brief summary of applicable legislation to water including requirements and divided by UK region. Due to frequent legislative developments users should check <**www.netregs.gov.uk**> when using the table.

Legislation	Key requirements	Direct site requirements	Indirect requirements	Application time planning/during construction/post
England				
Environmental Permitting Regulations (England & Wales) 2010 as amended	An environmental permit will be required for discharging to water to any controlled water or surface water drain. Also, a permit will describe any abstraction limits placed upon a site	Apply for an environmental permit before construction and do not exceed limits set within the permit	N/A	Planning During construction
Water Industry Act 1991	Consent is required from the local sewerage provider before discharging water to any foul water sewer	If any discharges are planned to any foul sewer then consent must be sought from the sewerage provider	N/A	Planning During construction

Legislation	Key requirements	Direct site requirements	Indirect requirements	Application time planning/during construction/post
The Environmental Damage (Prevention and Remediation) Regulations 2009	If any person or business carries out an activity that causes environmental damage they will have to remedy the damage. If there is a risk of damage from any business activities, it must prevented The regulations do not apply to environmental damage caused before the regulations came into force Overall, the regulations are likely to be used only for the most serious cases of damage Under the regulations, environmental damage is: ☐ serious damage to surface or groundwater ☐ contamination of land where there is a significant risk to human health ☐ serious damage to EU protected natural habitats and species or damage to SSSIs	If any activities threaten to cause, or have caused, environmental damage then: ☐ take steps to prevent the damage (or further damage) occurring ☐ inform the Environment Agency or other authorities who will provide information on how to prevent and/or remedy the damage If the Environment Agency or another authority has to remedy the damage then the company will be liable to pay the costs	N/A	Planning During construction Post construction
Groundwater (England & Wales) Regulations 2009	Empowers the Environment Agency to prevent direct or indirect discharge of certain dangerous substances to groundwater and control pollution resulting from the discharge of those and other substances	Do not discharge any substances to groundwater from site	N/A	During construction Post construction

Legislation	Key requirements	Direct site requirements	Indirect requirements	Application time planning/during construction/post
Wales				
Environmental Permitting Regulations (England & Wales) 2010 as amended	An environmental permit will be required for discharging to water to any controlled water or surface water drain. Also, a permit will describe any abstraction limits placed upon a site	Apply for an environmental permit before construction and do not exceed limits set within the permit	N/A	Planning During construction
Water Industry Act 1991	Consent is required from the local sewerage provider before discharging water to any foul water sewer	If any discharges are planned to any foul sewer then consent must be sought from the sewerage provider	N/A	Planning During construction

Legislation	Key requirements	Direct site requirements	Indirect requirements	Application time planning/during construction/post
Environmental Damage (Prevention and Remediation) (Wales) Regulations 2009	If any person or business carries out an activity that causes environmental damage then they will have to remedy the damage. If there is a risk of damage from any business activities, it must be prevented The regulations do not apply to environmental damage caused before the regulations came into force Overall, the regulations are likely to be used only for the most serious cases of damage Under the regulations, environmental damage is: ☐ serious damage to surface or groundwater ☐ contamination of land where there is a significant risk to human health ☐ serious damage to EU protected natural habitats and species or damage to SSSIs	If any activities threaten to cause, or have caused, environmental damage then: ☐ take steps to prevent the damage (or further damage) occurring ☐ inform the Environment Agency or other authorities who will provide information on how to prevent and/or remedy the damage If the Environment Agency or another authority has to remedy the damage then the company will be liable to pay the costs	N/A	Planning During construction Post construction
Groundwater (England & Wales) Regulations 2009	Empowers the Environment Agency to prevent direct or indirect discharge of certain dangerous substances to groundwater and control pollution resulting from the discharge of those and other substances.	Do not discharge any substances to groundwater from site	N/A	During construction Post construction

Legislation	Key requirements	Direct site requirements	Indirect requirements	Application time planning/during construction/post
Scotland				
Water Environment (Controlled Activities) (Scotland) Regulations 2005 (as amended by The Water Environment (Groundwater and Priority Substances) (Scotland) Regulations 2009	Abstraction or impoundment of water from surface, coastal or groundwater will most likely require a licence from SEPA. Also, this Regulation places limits on discharging to controlled water or a surface water drain and a licence must be obtained from SEPA. The Water Environment (Groundwater and Priority Substances) (Scotland) Regulations 2009, have amended this legislation to add a list of substances that may not be released to groundwater	If abstraction or impoundment is required, obtain a licence from SEPA and do not exceed the limits set	N/A	Planning During construction
Sewers Scotland Act 1968 (amended) 2002	Consent is required from the local sewerage provider before discharging water to any foul water sewer	If any discharges are planned to any foul sewer then consent must be sought from the sewerage provider	N/A	Planning During construction

Legislation	Key requirements	Direct site requirements	Indirect requirements	Application time planning/during construction/post
Environmental Liability (Scotland) Regulations 2009 SSI 266	If any person or business carries out an activity that causes environmental damage then they will have to remedy the damage. If there is a risk of damage from any business activities, it must be prevented The regulations do not apply to environmental damage caused before the regulations came into force Overall, the regulations are likely to be used only for the most serious cases of damage Under the regulations, environmental damage is: ☐ serious damage to surface or groundwater ☐ contamination of land where there is a significant risk to human health ☐ serious damage to EU protected natural habitats and species or damage to SSSIs	If any activities threaten to cause, or have caused, environmental damage then: ☐ take steps to prevent the damage (or further damage) occurring ☐ inform SEPA or other authorities who will provide information on how to prevent and/or remedy the damage If SEPA has to remedy the damage then the company will be liable to pay the costs	N/A	Planning During construction Post construction

Legislation	Key requirements	Direct site requirements	Indirect requirements	Application time planning/during construction/post
Northern Ireland				
Water Abstraction and Impoundment (Licensing) Regulations (Northern Ireland) 2006	Abstraction or impoundment of water from surface, coastal or groundwater will most likely require a licence from the Department of the Environment	If abstraction or impoundment is required, obtain a licence from the Department of the Environment and do not exceed the limits set	N/A	Planning During construction
The Water (Northern Ireland) Order 1999	Under the Act a consent must be sought from NIEA for discharge trade or sewage effluent to a waterway or into groundwater	If discharges are necessary from site then a consent must be sought from the NIEA	N/A	Planning During construction
Water and Sewerage Services (Northern Ireland) Order 2006	Consent is required from the local sewerage provider before discharging water to any foul water sewer	If any discharges are planned to any foul sewer then consent must be sought from the sewerage provider	N/A	Planning During construction

Legislation	Key requirements	Direct site requirements	Indirect requirements	Application time planning/during construction/post
Environmental Liability (Prevention and Remediation) Regulations (Northern Ireland) 2009	If any person or business carries out an activity that causes environmental damage then they will have to remedy the damage. If there is a risk of damage from any business activities, it must be prevented The regulations do not apply to environmental damage caused before the regulations came into force Overall, the regulations are likely to be used only for the most serious cases of damage Under the regulations, environmental damage is: ☐ serious damage to surface or groundwater ☐ contamination of land where there is a significant risk to human health ☐ serious damage to EU protected natural habitats and species or damage to ASSIs	If any activities threaten to cause, or have caused, environmental damage then: ☐ take steps to prevent the damage (or further damage) occurring ☐ inform NIEA or other authorities who will provide information on how to prevent and/or remedy the damage If NIEA has to remedy the damage then the company will be liable to pay the costs	N/A	Planning During construction Post construction
Groundwater (Northern Ireland) Regulations 2009	Empowers the DOE to prevent direct or indirect discharge of certain dangerous substances to groundwater and control pollution resulting from the discharge of those and other substances.	Do not discharge any substances to groundwater from site	N/A	During construction Post construction

UK environmental regulators, nature conservation and heritage bodies

Environmental regulators

Organisation	Responsibilities	Contact number	Website
Department of Environment Food and Rural Affairs (Defra)	Policy-maker for all aspects of the environment, rural matters, farming and food production at national level	08459 33 55 77	www.defra.gov.uk
Environment Agency (England and Wales)	Discharges to land and controlled water, waste, effluent discharges, abstraction licences some nature conservation functions, contaminated land, enforcing environmental legislation	08708 506 506	www.environment-agency.gov.uk
Northern Ireland Environment Agency (NIEA)	Discharges to land and controlled water, waste, nature conservation functions, contaminated land and the built heritage	028 9025 1477	www.ni-environment.gov.uk
Scottish Environment Protection Agency (SEPA)	Licensing discharges to the water environment, water abstractions, impoundments and river engineering activities, emissions to air and waste deposits to land. Duties with regards to sustainable development (climate change)	01786 457 700	www.sepa.org.uk
Local authority	Noise, air quality, traffic, the planning process and contaminated land. Some powers under waste legislation to stop, search waste carriers and confiscate vehicles		www.direct.gov.uk

Appendix A1

Statutory nature conservation organisations (SNCOs)

Organisation	Responsibilities	Contact number	Website
Countryside Council for Wales	National wildlife conservation authority and adviser on sustaining natural beauty	0845 1306 229	www.ccw.gov.uk
Natural England	Designated ecological sites, geological and geomorphological sites, and protected species	0845 600 3078	www.naturalengland.org.uk
Northern Ireland Environment Agency	Discharges to land and controlled water, waste, nature conservation functions, contaminated land and the built heritage	028 9025 1477	www.ni-environment.gov.uk
Scottish Natural Heritage	Designated ecological sites, geological and geomorphological sites, and protected species	01463 725 000	www.snh.org.uk

Heritage bodies

Organisation	Responsibilities	Contact number	Website
Cadw	Designated archaeological and heritage sites in Wales	01443 33 6000	www.cadw.wales.gov.uk
English Heritage	Responsible for protecting historic buildings, landscapes and archaeological sites	0870 333 1181	www.english-heritage.org.uk
Historic Scotland	Safeguarding the nation's built heritage	0131 668 8600	www.historic-scotland.gov.uk
Northern Ireland Environment Agency	Responsible for recording, protecting, conserving and promoting built heritage	028 9025 1477	www.ni-environment.gov.uk

Useful contacts

Organisation	Responsibilities	Contact number	Website
Chartered Institute of Environmental Health	Maintains and promotes improvements in public and environmental health	020 7928 6006	www.cieh.org
CIRIA	Operates across a range market sectors and disciplines offering a programme of research activities and publications for members and those involved with the delivery and operation of the built environment	020 7549 3300	www.ciria.org
Considerate Constructors Scheme	Voluntary code of practice for the construction industry	0800 783 1423	www.ccscheme.org.uk
Envirowise	Runs waste minimisation clubs, a free information helpline, case studies and good practice guides	0800 585794	www.envirowise.gov.uk
Health & Safety Executive	Advice on health and safety issues	0845 345 0055	www.hse.gov.uk
National Trust	Responsible for protecting historic buildings, landscapes and archaeological sites	0844 800 1895	www.nationaltrust.org.uk
National Trust for Scotland	Responsible for protecting historic buildings, landscapes and archaeological sites	0844 493 2100	www.nts.org.uk
NetRegs	Website run by Environment Agency detailing industry sector legislation	08708 506 506	www.netregs.gov.uk
Zero Waste Scotland	Funded by the Scottish Government to support delivery of its zero waste plan	01786 468 890	www.zerowastescotland.org.uk

Regulatory pollution prevention guidance notes

The Environment Agency, SEPA and the NIEA have produced a range of UK-wide Pollution Prevention Guidelines (PPGs). Each PPG is targeted at a particular industrial sector or activity and aims to provide advice on legal responsibilities and good environmental practice.

Copies of the PPGs can be downloaded from:

☐ Environment Agency <**www.environment-agency.gov.uk/ppg**>

☐ Net Regs <**www.netregs.gov.uk**>

The following table lists relevant PPGs and the section of this guide where they are referred to:

PPG	Title	Relevant topics
1	General guide to the prevention of pollution	4.9
2	Above ground oil storage tanks	4.6, 4.9
3	Use and design of oil separators in surface water drainage systems	4.9
4	Disposal of sewage where no mains drainage is available	4.9
5	Works and maintenance in or near water	4.9, 4.1
6	Working at construction and demolition sites	4.9
7	Refuelling facilities	4.9
8	Safe storage and disposal of used oils	4.5, 4.9
18	Managing fire water and major spillages	4.9
21	Incident response planning	2.4, 4.9
23	Maintenance of structures over water	4.9
26	Storage and handling of drums and intermediate bulk containers	4.5
27	Installation, decommissioning and removal of underground storage tanks	4.5

Details of further PPGs are available from the Environment Agency and NetRegs websites.